PASS

FAIL

PASS

*32 stories about teaching, from inspiring to hilarious
for anyone who has ever been to school*

FAIL

Edited by Kurt Kleidon and Rose A.O. Kleidon

**RED
SKY
BOOKS**

Akron, Ohio

Red Sky Books
Kleidon Publishing, Inc.

Red Sky books may be purchased in quantity for educational, business or sales promotional use. Please write Special Markets, Kleidon Publishing, Inc., 320 Springside Drive, Akron, Ohio 44333.

Cover design: Christie Lang
Interior layout: Tim Klinger

FIRST EDITION
Printed in the United States of America

10 9 8 7 6 5 4 3 2 1

TO

Dennis A. Kleidon
Professor Emeritus, Myers School of Art
The University of Akron

This book is dedicated to Dennis Kleidon, husband to
one of us and father to the other, whose unflagging
devotion to teaching inspired us and without whose
support this book would not have become a reality.

Contents

Preface   xi

Introduction: Beyond Instinct   xiii

1: Through the Classroom Door   1

My Students and Their Essays   3
    JOHN GUZLOWSKI

Let's Fight   5
    BARBARA SOMERS

No Wonder Your Paper's so Short!   9
    JULIANA GRAY VICE

Human Race   11
    BARBARA A. ROUILLARD

2: Was This on the Syllabus?   19

Chips off the Block   21
    MELINDA STILES

Some Things You Can Teach   25
    JESSICA GATES FREDRICKS

The Magician   29
    FRANZ WEINSCHENK

Unspoken Gratitude   31
    LISA JOHNSON

The Greatest Gift   35
    BRUCE BIRKEMEYER

3: Lesson Learned   39

I Hate Schools   41
CAROLYN S. KREMERS

A Teachable Moment   63
BEVERLY A. BUNCHER

A Brightly-Lit Room   67
MICHAEL O'ROURKE

Too Late for Miss Roselli   71
PRISCILLA LONG

4: Between the Lines   75

For Beth   77
BENJAMIN GROSSBERG

Callers   81
BARBARA A. ROUILLARD

Breakable Ashley   85
REBECCA J. KAISER

A Little Hopeful   87
JEFFERY LEE

Filed but Not Forgotten   95
MELINDA STILES

5: Sense and Nonsense   99

Tutoring with Richard   101
JAMES HEIN

Empty Gesture   107
MARILYN BATES

Miss Hotchkin, Racist   117
VICKI SALLOUM

Remembering Winter   135
CAROLYN HOWARD-JOHNSON

6: Teacher's Guide   141

A Curmudgeon's Book of Lists: Take Two   143
RICHARD HAGUE

High Plains Drifter   147
MICHAEL O'ROURKE

Chicago Urban Skills Institute: a Valiant Effort, 1978   153
MARION STERN

The Former Student   159
MARK VINZ

Charming the Bridge Over the River   165
SHELLEY KITTREDGE FROST

A Hasty Conclusion   171
THOMAS POPP

7: Dancing Through Life   179

Tales from the Tanning Bed   181
BETH WALKER

Pencilhead   185
SARAH A. POWLEY

One Lone Teacher and His Trusty Red Pen   189
BRAD HAKES

Trouble, Mess, Disaster   195
RICHARD HAGUE

About our Authors   199

Preface

In *Pass/Fail,* Red Sky Books proudly present the winners of the 2001 Red Sky Writing Competition: Twenty-eight writers who are or have been teachers and who testify brilliantly to the failures and the triumphs, the despair and the heartwarming rewards that come with one of the world's most challenging professions, teaching.

Red Sky Books salutes each of the writers chosen for inclusion in this anthology. The excellence of their writing was evaluated by the following distinguished group of jurors, members of the faculty at the University of Akron in Akron, Ohio:

Robert Dial, Ph.D., Associate Professor of English

Rose A.O. Kleidon, M.A.T.E., Professor Emeritus, English

Sally K. Slocum, Ph.D.

 Associate Professor Emeritus of English

James D. Switzer, M.A., Professor Emeritus, English

Sheldon Wrice, Ph.D., Associate Professor, English

Red Sky Books takes its name from the saying, "Red Sky at night, sailor's delight; red sky in the morning, sailor take warning." Those of us at the helm of Red Sky Books are sailors, which gives us an inordinate fondness for all things salty.

More important, the saying reflects our appreciation for those who have the good sense to notice the world around them and the good judgment to interpret it thoughtfully.

For more information about Red Sky Books, visit our web site at www.kleidon.com.

We acknowledge the following publishers and individuals for permission to print or reprint these stories:

Carolyn S. Kremers' "I Hate Schools" is an edited excerpt from *Pretend People: Gifts from a Yup'ik Eskimo Village*. ©1996 by Carolyn Kremers, with permission from Alaska Northwest Books.

Carolyn Howard-Johnson's "Remembering Winter" first appeared in slightly different form in *Harkening*.

Richard Hague's "A Curmudgeon's Book of Lists: Take Two" and "Trouble, Mess, Disaster" first appeared in slightly different form in *Word Magazine*.

"Too Late for Miss Roselli" is used with the author's permission. ©2001 by Priscilla Long. The complete version of the story will appear as "Dropout" in *Stonework and Other Work: Creative Nonfictions* by Priscilla Long, scheduled for publication in 2002.

Introduction: Beyond Instinct

> The ideal condition would be, I admit,
>
> that men should be right by instinct;
>
> but since we are all likely to go astray,
>
> the reasonable thing is to learn from those who
>
> can teach.

—SOPHOCLES

To the question, "What makes us human?" there are many answers, but none truer than: "We are those who teach."

It is the nature of human beings to go beyond instinct, to want and need more than instinct as a guide. This means we teach our young, but it also means that we expect to learn throughout our lives, and that to do so, we depend on others – teachers of one kind or another – to lead us. We teach against all odds; we teach even when reluctant to do so; we teach badly and brilliantly; everybody teaches. Teaching has been going on as long as there have been human beings. You would think we would know how to do it perfectly by now.

In America, about a century ago, we began a grand experiment intended to lift every student into an organized setting where he or she could learn more than fields, factories, families and streets teach. Today, almost every American has been in school, and

. most, for many years. If we were to grade on effort, we would have to give our country an A.

Our grade for achievement has been less salutary. About 15% of our people are still illiterate. A century ago, comprehension and skill in even rudimentary math and science was rare; today, except for a cluster of engineers, scientists and accountants, it still is.

Perhaps most surprising, considering the heroism of the attempt, is that the experience of teaching and learning has been so painful for so many of the people involved. How can our good intentions have produced such mixed results? Although we can point to much success, the mystery is that we also should have caused so much misery.

Across the nation, school buildings are falling apart. Do we have the will to rebuild? If we do muster the willpower and the cash, we may make the mistake of building what we needed yesterday. Some say that the time has come to teach in new ways, replacing classrooms entirely.

Teaching and learning are core human activities, whether they occur in shady groves of olives, in brightly lit classrooms (so often painted with unconscious irony in shades of olive) or by the dim light of computer screens.

We must learn *now* to identify, understand and enrich the heart of teaching and learning. Because, one way or the other, the next generation will be taught.

🍎

In this year, 2001, more than 33,000 schools, colleges and universities across America are engaged in teaching students of all ages and every description.

Studies about education pour out of graduate schools and government agencies. Education issues are debated at every level on boards and in councils, among teachers and students, administrators and parents, candidates and legislators, in courts and on editorial pages.

Somewhere amid all of this we should have a chance to be quiet and listen to authentic voices of teachers. This small volume gives you that opportunity.

—ROSE A.O.KLEIDON

CHAPTER ONE

Through the Classroom Door

The future of civilization is...being written
in the classrooms of the world.

–Milton L. Smith

2 •

JOHN GUZLOWSKI

My Students and Their Essays

They come with papers on Down's syndrome
Euthanasia, grandfathers dying
Of inoperable liver cancer, the stresses
That break young people down
And turn them into zombies or suicides,
Alcoholics with no way out but more booze.

I smooth the pages, pat them into neat piles
And say, "Here, here you need a comma; there
A hyphen, and don't forget to cite your sources
And alphabetize correctly the works cited."

But this isn't what I want to say. I want
To tell them the lies I want to tell myself:
Don't worry, things will get better, life
Turns the corner, the sun shines through.

4 •

BARBARA SOMERS

Let's Fight

"I can fight as good as any boy," said Wanda. She was a sweet-looking thirteen-year-old.

"Why would you fight?" I asked.

"Ohmigod. What if someone says something bad about your mother? You gotta fight. It's your mother."

"But," I protested, "you told me you don't like your mother. So why fight?"

"Ya gotta. You just gotta. And if someone says something bad about your little brother or sister, you gotta fight them too."

"Lookit," said Maddie. "I just got off probation for fighting."

Maddie was a beautiful girl, very sweet and quiet. She looked so angelic I wished I could hang her on a Christmas tree as an ornament. Probation and Maddie just didn't make sense.

"Not you, Maddie," I said. "You fighting? Why? What happened?"

"She said something bad about my little brother so I hit her."

"Well. OK. But probation? I don't get it."

"They had to take her off in an ambulance. I guess that's why

5

I got probation," she said softly.

I was really shocked and told the group so. They were eager to educate me.

"If someone tries to take your boyfriend away, even if you don't like him anymore, you gotta fight her," continued Wanda.

"But if you no longer want that boyfriend, why would you need to fight the next girl?" I asked.

"Ohmigod," said Carla. "You just gotta."

"And then," continued Carla, "what if someone has an attitude? You have to fight."

Again the group agreed. Yup. You gotta fight.

I felt as if I was falling through the looking glass into a world I didn't know existed.

"Well, what's an attitude?" I asked.

"An attitude," said Wanda, "You know. When someone has an attitude on you. You know. So then you fight."

The girls nodded. They knew but I didn't. "Give me an example," I said.

"Ohmigod. What if someone looks at you funny? What if someone, you know, pushes you, sort of? What if someone says something mean? That's an attitude. So then you gotta fight." Carla was out of breath from her explaining.

"Well, couldn't you talk it over with the person? Does it have to be a fight? Can't you talk as we do here in class?" I asked.

The girls' tongues clicked against the roofs of their mouths. They were about to give up on me as a hopeless case.

"Hey, look," said Wanda. "We gotta fight. But first we have to get ready."

"How?" I asked.

"Ohmigod," she continued. "You have to take off your earrings. Otherwise they'll tear your ears open. Then you pull your hair into a very tight knot. That's so they can't pull your hair out. Then you put thick grease all over your face and arms. That's so if they're using a knife or razor, it'll slide off and won't be able to cut you. Then you're ready."

Again the girls nodded in agreement. That's it, all right.

"Girls," I pled. "Talking. Not fighting. Try it. Just think. No probation. No punishment. No lumps or bruises. Try it. You'll see."

"Ohmigod," said Wanda. "You don't get it."

She's right. I don't. Maybe next week when we get together, I'll be more successful.

No Wonder Your Paper's So Short!

During my first year as a graduate student, I worked as a tutor in the university's writing center. Our tutees ran the gamut, from the hyper-overachiever who will be unable to live with anything less than an A+ to those who'd been sentenced to tutoring by their instructors or coaches.

One afternoon, a freshman of the latter variety lumbered in. He had a first draft of a paper he'd written on a poem by Aphra Behn, and wanted someone to "look it over" (read: "fix it"). After I located the textbook (of course, he had not brought his book with him), I sat beside the student and glanced at his paper. It was only a page and a half long.

"This looks a little short," I said.

"Yeah," he grunted. "That's what I need help with. I can't think of anything else to say."

Visions of an hour spent coaxing interpretations from a student who wanted me to spoon-feed him the rest of his paper swam before my eyes. I suppressed a sigh and gathered my resolve. "Well," I said, "I'm not familiar with this poem, so let me read it over, and then we'll look at your paper and see what we can come up with."

He nodded, and I opened the book to the poem. At the bottom of the right-hand page were the title, a four-line stanza, and two more lines, ending with a period. I read each line carefully, noting the meter, rhyme, diction and other points I could bring to my tutee's attention. Then I turned the page.

I heard a gasp, followed by "oh." My heart sank, but I finished the poem – another two lines and another four-line stanza – before looking up at the student. He looked utterly bewildered, like a zebra that cannot quite comprehend the lion already feeding on its innards.

"You didn't turn the page," I said. It was not a question.

He shook his head. "I thought it was finished. There was a period."

This time, my sigh was audible.

BARBARA A. ROUILLARD

The Human Race

Later, my best friend Jenny told me, "Welcome to the human race."

Later, my student Jimmy told me, "Holy shit! I was in Miss Parker's room across the hall, and I heard you – you were really up front with Mr. Morgan."

Later, Mary, the teacher/counselor in the Student Support Center told me that the same thing happened to her this year. She said, "I overheard a few kids say, 'Let's go down to Food Lab and get some of the retards to put on a show for us.'"

Now, I'm squatting by the fire exit in the back hall between my classroom and the upper library. I'm squatting on my haunches and leaning against the wall. The brick feels cool, but my face is hot and steamy because I'm crying.

I'm crying and watching Kevin for the umpteenth time race down the hall and then return to me.

"Get in the room, Kevin. Start your assignment."

"No, Rouillard, I want to stay here with you. I want to help you. I tried to help you, didn't I?"

"If you want to help me now, go back in our room."

How did I end up on this Monday morning, squatting by the fire exit, crying? It really started Friday.

🍎

Friday, fourth period.

Sarah enters the room and starts. All I can hear is her yelling – that booming, foul mouth. All I've heard for the last six months is that voice.

"Don't get in your groups," she shouts. "Sit wherever you want. Don't be such wusses. She's just a fucking teacher."

The kids don't move. They look around undecidedly.

"Sarah, quit!" I yell back.

But she keeps it up. My face close to hers; I hear myself say at almost a whisper, "I don't like you, Sarah."

"Who gives a shit?" she answers. "I don't like you either."

"Good. Now that we understand each other, we can get on with our jobs – I teach, you learn."

"Fuck you."

"You're out!"

She exits. I collapse at my desk. The kids get down to work. Later, after lunch, Ryan Morgan, the disciplinary vice principal, sits beside me at my desk. "Sarah," he begins, " said you called her a lesbo."

I want to laugh at this absurdity, but indignation spews from my mouth: "What is she, nuts? If that stupid kid had bothered this year to get to know me at all, she would have figured out I don't need one of those rainbow triangle decals on my door – safe zone for gay, lesbian, bisexual, transgender students – for cripes' sake, Ryan, I live it!"

Ryan smiles and adds, "Sarah says everyone swears all the time in your room."

"Sarah should talk. Her mouth is the worst I've ever heard."

"Well. Talk to Sarah, please." Ryan rises to leave. "And for now on, write up any kid who swears. You don't have to take that shit. Write them up for profanity."

"OK," I answer and laugh at the irony of Ryan's word choice.

There's a reason I never write up a kid. Actually there are two reasons. The first reason is that I don't want to bother Ryan. He has a whole school to deal with, not just special ed. Short of a student laying hands on another kid, I handle our own problems.

Secondly, there's my pride. I've never turned a kid away or told my big boss, the town's special ed. administrator, that a kid is too hard for me. Not in seventeen years.

Monday.

The kids in first, second, and third periods take the news fairly well. "No more swearing," I tell them. "Don't slip. Mr. Morgan says to write up anyone who swears."

Now it's time for fourth period and Sarah enters.

"Go to your group," I tell her. "I need everyone to sit down. I need to speak with you all."

Sarah sits, leans back in her chair, and slams her feet up on one of the tables.

"From tomorrow on, Mr. Morgan wants everyone who swears to be written up for profanity." Before I can continue, Sarah is on her feet.

"It's because of me." Her head bobs and dips like a prizefighter's. "Because she called me a lesbo and got me in trouble, she's gonna slam us. What an asshole!"

The room is silent. I smack my hands to my thighs. The only sound I can hear, the sound that echoes in my head, is that slap of my palms on my leg muscles. "Well, you did it, Sarah. I was trying to protect you. I was just going to tell you Mr. Morgan's orders, and then we could get down to work. You did it."

"No, you did it. You called me a lesbo. You heard her. Right Mercedes?" Sarah turns her squinting, mascara-drenched eyes on Mercedes. Mercedes looks down and nods. "You heard her. Right, Aaron?" Aaron won't raise his hand, but nods "yes," and so does Sue. I am speechless.

But Kevin is on his feet, and running from table to table. "She didn't say it. She didn't say it. I didn't hear her say it."

"Shut up, you little fucker," Sarah yells at Kevin. "You weren't here on Friday; you were suspended. Besides, I already went to the principal with my mother this morning. And if that doesn't work I'll go to the superintendent.

"That's enough, Sarah." I call the office. I pull the phone cord into the hallway. "Ryan, this is it. I need Sarah out now. She's yelling that I called her a lesbo. I won't go to that yahoo principal Fetters. I won't sit and explain that I didn't do this and I didn't do that. I won't. I won't give that brat any more power. 'No, Dr. Fetters, I didn't call her that name,' blah, blah, blah and explain and justify and validate any of that monster's feelings or thoughts. She's not even acting human!"

"I'll be right down," Ryan answers. He's there in two minutes flat. "Let's go," he says and points at Sarah.

"She calls me a lesbo, and I get punished. I'm calling my mother."

"You're right, you're calling your mother. Out!" Ryan's voice is deafening.

The door slams. No one says a word.

🍎

I walk to my desk. Okay, the world history group is supposed to read pages 201-205 and then do questions 1-5, and I feel it, I feel it coming: I burst into tears.

"I have to leave," I speak to my aide, Marie. I'm out the door before she can answer and sitting in the hall by the fire exit with Kevin running back and forth down the hall. It's the first time in all my seventeen years here I've cried.

Kevin and I return. My face is hot and flushed, "You heard me say that?" I question Mercedes, Aaron, and Sue. Not one of them looks up, but they shake their heads "no."

Sue bursts into tears. "I hate her. I hate her. I hate her."

I sit. It is quiet. The bell rings. I leave my room and stop at Jenny's. "Welcome to the human race," She tells me.

"If they're looking for me, I'm leaving the grounds for about a half an hour," I tell Ryan's secretary as I head out the door. I drive the ten minutes to the post office, smoke in my car, then drive back to the school.

I head straight for Ryan's office. He begins: "I met with Sarah and her mom. Sarah was sent home with her mother. Sarah went nuts and said the kids smoke in your room." My mouth drops open. "Then she said they don't smoke in your room. Then she said how you were her favorite teacher until you married that guy and changed. She knows you don't like her."

"I know," I answer. "I told her I don't like her. I asked her, 'Why would I like you when you abuse me? I'm not emotionally disturbed.' But I also told her that that doesn't mean we can't do our jobs."

"The kids want and need you to like them. It's important to them that you like them. Let's meet tomorrow with Sarah."

"Ryan, you know I'm not listening to you, but I'll hear you when I get home." He smiles. "Ryan, I want to make out a new schedule for Sarah."

"Let's meet first, please," Ryan pleads.

I went home and was in my pajamas by three-thirty. I thought of Sarah – the bleached blonde spikes to her hair, her foul mouth, her swagger. "I want to go back to Missouri. Massachusetts sucks." I thought of Sarah. Find one thing you like about her. I fell to sleep with nothing.

Tuesday.

Sarah and I sit, side by side, in front of Ryan's desk. Ryan begins, "Sarah, we need to look at the past few days and then decide what to do with your program."

Sarah interrupts him. "I want to graduate. I can't leave Miss Rouillard's room. I can't take regular ed. history."

"Hold on, Sarah," Ryan interrupts. "You want to start, Ms. Rouillard?"

"Sarah, I did not call you that name."

"Yes, you did."

"No, I didn't." I continue over her protests. "Yesterday Mr.

Morgan told me that he thought you needed to know that I liked you. Unfortunately, I don't. But last night it occurred to me that you haven't given me a chance to like you." Then it hits me. "Sarah, I just thought of something. I like that you call fourth period, "fourth hour." I think it's funny."

Sarah smiles and then blurts out, "I never would have said I didn't like you if you hadn't said it first. I like you." Then she begins to weep. "I'm sorry."

🍎

Sarah will be given another chance. As I told her, "The good thing about being human is that as long as they haven't nailed down the lid, we can always start over again."

For seventeen years, I've buried my ego at work. How else could I not take it personally when a kid, venting anger, calls me names, swears and screams in my face?

For seventeen years, I've told myself that I'm here for the kids, the kids aren't here for me. And for seventeen years I thought I knew that I was important to them, but I didn't really know or I guess I had forgotten:

As Jenny would say, "Welcome to the human race."

CHAPTER TWO

Was This on the Syllabus?

That which we do not call education is more precious than that which we call so.

—RALPH WALDO EMERSON

MELINDA STILES

Chips Off the Block

Leroy Shane didn't care a whit about school and never did a lick of homework. I liked him a lot. I talked to him, sent home progress reports, and left messages at his house, which were never returned. His parents didn't make it to conferences. Leroy earned an honest F in English. The day after report cards were sent home, I received a call in the lounge during lunch. Swallowing a bite of egg salad, I answered. "Hello?"

"This is Mrs. Shane, and I'm not very happy. I have Leroy's report card here, and he had all F's."

"I can speak about English. Have you received any of my messages or progress reports?"

"I didn't call to talk about that. I'm very upset, and I want these grades changed!"

"Leroy will have to..."

"Don't you know he has numb spots on his brain?" She started sobbing and yelling incoherently.

I held the phone away from my ear. My colleagues looked in my direction. "You're going to have to call back when you're calm," I said and hung up. Sitting back down I shook my head. What the heck are numb spots on the brain?

🍎

Sylvia Page was in my honors English class. She was beautiful and bright but always looked tired. She missed nine classes the first six weeks of school. I was glad to see her mother at my desk for conferences. As always, I started with a positive comment. Then I had the audacity to say, "I'm worried that Sylvia has missed nine days. She's frustrated with all the make-up work. I hate to see her overloaded. Is there something we can do to help her?"

Mrs. Page glared at me and stood. "Do you think it will be engraved on her tombstone that she missed your class nine times?!" she shrieked.

I'd read the books on how to conduct effective conferences but the answer to this question was never discussed. I could only stare at her, my mouth agape.

She let fly a flood of words punctuated with profanities. Spittle frothed from the corners of her mouth. Tears etched mascara tracks down her cheeks. When she told me I had no idea how lucky I was to have these honor students, I stood up and told her the conference was over. She turned on her heel, snapped her head around and marched off.

A colleague had observed the exchange and walked to my desk. "I see you caught the wrath of Mrs. Page. Forget about it. She will. She's drunk."

I was more worried than ever about Sylvia.

🍎

Gary was a sophomore who cried a lot in class. Admittedly, I found this irritating. When I tried to talk to him about it, he cried. The tears would flow when I asked him about an assignment he didn't turn in or when I turned a deaf ear to his litany of excuses. My standard response was, "Gary, you're very bright, but your English grade doesn't show it. I don't want your excuses. I want your assignments."

Gary's father, who tipped the scale at well over 300 pounds, showed up at fall conferences. He walked to my desk and stood over me. He was a DJ with a booming voice. "You and my son have a big problem, and I want to know what you're going to do about it."

"Why don't you have a seat, and we'll discuss it."

He took a step closer. His voice increased by decibels. "I don't want to sit down. You talk to me now and tell me what your problem is."

I stood up, dwarfed by this giant among men. "I'm afraid we can't have a conference if you insist on yelling."

I probably shouldn't have been shocked when he sat down, apologized, and then started crying.

JESSICA GATES FREDRICKS

Some Things You Can Teach

Two rival gangs attended the school where I spent my first year as a band director. As a result the inner-city high school was regularly spray-painted with gang messages and threats. Once I returned to find bullet holes riddling my classroom door – not the best start to a Monday morning.

Pep rallies were always held in the gym and presented obvious discipline problems for an already rowdy student body. The rallies, usually during Friday's last period, tended to bring out the worst in our students.

At one pep rally, the principal invited representatives from student clubs to speak. The Student Council president took the microphone to jeers and the Spanish Club officers received spitballs and paper airplanes. Even the football team – a source of pride for both the school and the community – was taunted and booed.

Watching the spectacle, I felt ashamed and a little disgusted. What is the point of educating students who lack a moral compass, a sense of decent behavior? Our purpose as teachers is not just to teach reading and math, but also to teach the skills of humanity.

Our principal felt the best way to teach such life skills was to lead by example. Those of us who agreed made a point of exhibiting compassion, kindness and fair-mindedness in our daily activities. Looking around the noisy gym, I felt our efforts to communicate these things to the students had been distinctly unsuccessful.

As our principal called the last club, my heart sank – it was the Special Olympics team.

Our school had a very active Special Olympics team. They practiced every day in the school cafeteria one hour before lunch. Despite having severe physical and mental disabilities, the team was a tight-knit group of dedicated members. This made it hard to watch all 27 students on the Special Olympics team make their way to the gym floor.

They moved slowly, some with odd gaits or limbs held at awkward angles, but all with determination and purpose.

I cringed, expecting the worst. A small group of high school students can be brutal, and this particular group was very large and very rambunctious. If they took such delight in making fun of the school's best athletes, what would they do to the Special Olympics team?

The captain took the microphone. Greg was a tall, lanky senior with Ashbury's Syndrome.

"We...are...the...Special Olympics team," Greg said in slow, measured phrases.

Amazingly, the student body was silent. Not one jeer emerged, not one spitball flew. The melee was still. They seemed to be entranced by the energy emanating from the 27 teammates before them, teammates who were not afraid to be themselves. Laughing and jostling each other in ways that were perfectly natural to them but oddly unnatural to the student body, the teammates were a picture of happiness.

Greg continued. "We...have...a game...Saturday night. Come... out... and... see...us!" Greg pumped an arm awkwardly into the air and emitted a hoarse yell, encouraging the student body to join him.

A pregnant pause ensued, during which I feared the student body would turn, reverting to their former jeering selves.

Instead, a thunderous roar erupted from the bleachers. Genuine cheers were shouted, and every student wore a smile. The Special Olympics team jumped up and down, pumping fists to no particular beat except their own.

The cheering continued for several minutes, at which time the principal had to usher the Special Olympics team off the gym floor in order to quiet the crowd.

My own face was streaked with tears of joy, tears falling in disbelief at the inexorable kindness that exists in the human spirit. There are some things you can teach, and there are some things you've already taught.

FRANZ WEINSCHENK

The Magician

After I retired from teaching, I took a job as the Executive
Director of the Volunteer Bureau of Fresno County. Among
other things, we worked with the probation department, who
sent us convicted persons who had to put in community service
hours as a part of their sentence.

One week, looking over the list, I recognized the name of a
former student of mine, Neil. He wasn't much in class, but he was
one of the uncanniest basketball players I have ever seen play
anywhere. Of course, the prevailing thinking was then and still is
now that if you're an uncanny basketball player, you don't need
to be much in class.

The other kids called him, "The Magician." When Neil came
to the Volunteer Bureau for his placement, I hardly recognized
him. True, it had been more than thirty years, but he looked so
feeble – so totally gray, all hunched over and shaking, his cheeks
drawn in, his body sagging, his sunken eyes swimming in sadness,
no spirit left at all – lost in a narcotic dream.

It took me back to a Friday night at the high school gymnasium. With the game tied and only seconds to go, our cheering section right behind me was screaming so loudly and relentlessly that the noise became almost physically painful. Everyone knew Coach had told his players to give the ball to Neil as we watched him dribble down the court. We could tell our opponents sensed that Neil was the team's best player. He wasn't going to pass off the ball. They knew they had to either stop him or lose.

Neil surveyed the opposition and smiled. With seconds ticking away, he stopped and started; dribbled in and out looking for a weakness, backed off quickly, then leapt forward, turned and faked a shot. When his defender leapt up to block the shot, he deftly changed direction, circled around him as quick as a cat and shot the ball. Swish! The game was over. Delirium!

Narcotics are serious. The judge could have given him hard time but put him on probation with community service. "Remember me, Neil?" I asked. "I used to be your teacher." But he only turned away sadly. I made sure he got a good placement, but it was too late.

Neil couldn't out-dribble his demons. Arrested several times more, in and out of jails and drug treatment centers, his picture soon appeared among those we mourn at class reunions. All that magic laid to rest.

LISA JOHNSON

Unspoken Gratitude

Michael, rubbing the hairs of his new goatee, joined the semi-circle with the other students. He always sat in the back row alone, but I'd finally coaxed him into helping me with the day's activity. In the quiet, his hands fidgeted. Then Brenda spoke.

"Do people tease you ever?"

I was afraid for his answer. "Yes, all the time in middle school." He stared at her. "But I've grown out of it now." I didn't believe it. How does one outgrow the taste of cruelty?

"That's so wrong," someone said. The room fell silent again. Michael scraped the corner of his desk with a pen, looking downward. Then Steve, a shy kid, cleared his throat.

"What's your favorite sign?"

Michael shrugged.

"I'll tell you mine," his interpreter answered. "Captivating." Her eyes widened as her fingers wiffled though the air, meeting in the center of her body.

"I know." Michael decided to respond. "Touch the way." He signed it quickly.

"Do it again," they said. It was the first time we'd seen him sign. He always just read lips and talked, embarrassed of his deafness.

In repetition, the words and signing became a graceful song. The class was fascinated.

"How many sign languages are there?"

"If you were born deaf, why did it take so long for anyone to notice?"

"Can you play sports?"

"They were asking so fast he couldn't answer. He smiled. They were paying attention to him, finally.

"Why don't you have your driver's license?"

"If only your mom uses sign language, how do you communicate with your dad and sister?"

"Sign your name." He did. This was better than anything I'd thought of. We'd already walked around the halls blindfolded and drawn trees with a pen in our mouths, trying to find ways to experience what being handicapped was like, even if for just a few minutes.

People in the department complained about my students. Though tenth graders, it was said that they had the reading ability of eight-year-olds. And forget social skills, grumbled more than a few colleagues.

But these kids were now getting beneath the surface in ways the rest of us would never have. We'd have been too afraid, too tactful. And Michael was responding.

Several of them said they'd like to learn sign language.

"Why don't you start a club?" That was Brenda again. " I would join!"

"Me too!"

"I could help," Brenda continued. "I'll go around and tell everybody I know. A lot of people would be interested."

This was the first time I'd seen Michael perk up. I remembered hearing that once a month his parents paid someone to have pizza with him.

Emerson once said, "What you do speaks so loud that I cannot hear what you say." How do you thank someone for noticing a person who really needs to be seen? That day, I didn't know how to express my intense gratitude to the students. I could only stammer goodbye at the end of class.

34 •

The Greatest Gift

The bell rang. A hundred plus students scrambled to their seats in third hour study hall, some fifty to each side of me in the rectangular room. My eyes seemed to be pulled to one student in particular. He was straight ahead of me in the back row. I took roll and signed the passes of students going to see a teacher for help, to a science lab or to a band lesson. With these duties out of the way, I tried to read some student papers as the study hall settled down for an hour of serious academic work.

But my eyes kept returning to the kid in the back row. Every time I looked at him he was looking at me. Not the look that said, "As soon as he stops looking at me, I'll fire off my spitball at Henry" or the look that said, "When the old goat gets distracted, I'll slip out for a cigarette," but just a look. I gave him the come-here gesture with my finger. He came up and got down on one knee beside me at the desk.

It was then I realized I did not know what I wanted to say. After a pause, I took out a note pad and started writing a column of words that I thought described him. He was in one of my speech classes so we were not total strangers. After 14 or 16 words like intelligent, strong, independent, talented, leader, good-looking, and bullheaded, he took the pen out of my hand, made a bracket that grouped all the words together and to the right of the column penned, "suicide."

I looked at him. He went back to his desk and brought up his notebook. He opened it to the last page for me, and I read backwards through the pages his dated suicide notes.

On the bottom of his notebook I wrote, "Promise me you won't do anything until I have a chance to talk to you."

He agreed.

🍎

Two days later in study hall I wrote him a note asking him to come to my place after football practice. I wanted to take him out for supper. He nodded.

We drove toward a nearby town to eat, after our decision that it would be best to have our talk away from friends and nosey eavesdroppers. On the way over I told him that before we got started on his concerns, I had a problem. I wasn't sure what I wanted to do with another student and wondered if he would give me an opinion.

"Shoot," he said.

So I told him about a former student who called me at 2:00 AM from college, crying and not knowing what to do. When my story was over, he sat up, looking straight ahead, and said with conviction, "I'd tell him to buck up, stop feeling sorry for himself, face the reality of it, and move on with his life. He shouldn't be expecting things to come his way on a silver platter, without any trouble on his part. You know what they say: 'life isn't a rose garden.'"

He froze.

Turning to look at me with eyes as focused as an eagle's on its prey, he hushed, "Would be good advice for me, huh? You tricked me."

I could not resist a small smile and asked, "Where do you want to eat?"

After supper we headed for home, but not by the way we had come. I was taking a detour for a purpose. Eventually, he asked, "Where we goin'?"

"You'll see." I said, as I drove down gravel country roads looking for the spot that was known to be the highest hill in the county. It was a clear fall night. With no moon, the night would have been pitch black, had it not been for the many bright stars. I pulled off the road onto a field entrance, stopping before a gate. We got out, jumped the fence and climbed to the top of the hill. The air moved gently from the north with a hint of chill.

"You know," I said in the tone of an old man reminiscing, "when you look at all those stars, it makes you realize how insignificant we really are – each of us like a speck of dust. If you commit suicide, I don't think the galaxies out there are going to notice, much less care. You are just too insignificant to bring the universe to its knees in sorrow.

"Yet, as we stand here, looking at it all, you have something the stars, mighty as they are, don't even get to ask for.

"God gave you life, the greatest gift there is. What more do you have the right to ask for? In this moment, at the front end of your life, you may not know why He created you, but do you really think you are in a position to question His judgment?"

It was a beautiful night.

We walked back to the truck and drove home in silence. Before he got out of the truck, I made him promise to talk to his folks. He did not have to show them his notebook, but he had to tell them what was bothering him.

He promised he would, and he kept his promise. I asked him to meet with a counselor, and he met with her regularly.

For the rest of his sophomore year, we talked once a week and after that as he felt the need, sometimes with a knock on my door in the middle of the night. Once he asked me, "Who do you talk to?"

"Eighty-year-olds," I said, "or at least someone who has been down this path before."

"Guess I'll be needing someone all my life," he said. "You too?"

"Yes," I said, "me too."

CHAPTER THREE

Lesson Learned

If I had a child who wanted to be a teacher,
I would bid him Godspeed as if he were
going to a war. The war against prejudice,
greed and ignorance is eternal.

—JAMES HILTON

CAROLYN S. KREMERS

excerpted from

I Hate Schools

I stood in Room 311, staring out the window at the tracks of the Chicago and Western Railway. Fifth Period had ended. Sounds of the school bell and of teenagers talking and laughing as they pecked at piano keys on their way out had subsided and disappeared.

I began doing what I did every day at that time. Coming down. I relaxed the muscles in my head and shoulders and took a deep breath. I let my mind disengage itself from the events of the morning's three classes, let it step back, view the morning as a whole, take note of what had happened and what hadn't and why, then forget it. There was still the afternoon to be tackled: hall-duty, planning period, Girls' Chorus, and one more General Music class.

I glanced around the room. Funny, what a sense of accomplishment that empty, orderly room could give. Thirty desks were still in rows that a few students and I had arranged that morning when, as every morning, we arrived and the room looked as if a tornado had blown through. Whoever used the room later in the day must have had one wild class. So far about eight desks had been struck down in the line of duty, their collapsible tops broken or bent so they couldn't be raised to write on. These desks were piled at the back in the left corner. A few Venetian blinds had also been destroyed, a nuisance when one wanted to show a filmstrip. A bigger nuisance, though, was the window in the right corner. Its frame was so bent that it could not be closed.

One day during class, two janitors had come in with a sheet of Visqueen and a roll of duct tape and had covered the window. I wondered how that would help in ten-degree weather.

"I know duct tape is no solution," the head janitor had said, when I asked, "but there's sixty-three windows like that in this building, and the principal said we had to do something."

I was able to keep students away from the tape by putting the storage cupboard under the window.

Ah, that cupboard. After begging the head janitor for a month, I had succeeded in getting a key to lock it. Inside was a place to keep all the materials I had scrounged since September: nine illustrated music textbooks written at eighth-grade level, two packages of construction paper, some glossy photos of musical instruments clipped from magazines and sales brochures, and several boxes of crayons, colored pencils, and pastels.

If the small cupboard and the key were a victory, the big cupboard with the padlock, at the front of the room, was a miracle. Its contents, a thousand-dollar stereo system, had been in storage in the school basement for a year. One afternoon at a music department meeting, the chairperson had mentioned that stereo systems had been ordered for each of the four music rooms in the new school. The systems had not been installed yet, however, because parts were missing. "Or something," said the chair.

We got a technician from the factory to come to the school and inspect the equipment. There were four five-foot-tall stereo transceivers with automatic turntables and outlets for headphones and tape recorders, and four pairs of three-foot-tall mahogany speakers on wheels. The technician assured the music chairperson that the equipment was ready to install.

"Okay," the chair said, turning to me. "Looks like all you need to do is ask the janitors to move a system into your classroom."

I tried.

"Ain't no safe place to put that thing," said the head janitor. "Till there is, that stereo ain't going nowhere."

He must have seen my disappointment. "Well, you could keep it in the library and have some students wheel it over to your room when you need it."

"Are you crazy? Move that system in and out everyday? Do you know what that would do to it?"

"Well, you find a cupboard big enough to store it in, and we'll move it."

I started keeping an eye out for cupboards seven feet tall and five feet wide. I found one in the library and talked the librarian into giving it up. The janitors moved it to the third floor, only to move it down again when the librarian discovered that the principal had not ordered hers moved. He had simply said, "Find one."

"We don't need this cupboard now, but in two years when all our audio-visual materials arrive, we will, and we probably won't be able to get another one then. I better keep this," she said.

At last I located an empty cupboard in the chorus room.

"We can't move this," the head janitor said. "It's too heavy. Anyway, it won't fit through your door."

He looked at me. "Okay, okay. Here's a cupboard you can use. It just has a few nuts and bolts in it, nothing important. I guess we can let you have it."

The cupboard was moved to the third floor and, after another week, the padlock was on and the stereo system installed. It was beautiful. It was a miracle.

"Hey, where'd you get that?!"

"Wow, is that your stereo, Miss Kremers?"

"Gee, how much did that thing cost?"

"When can we play it?"

"Will ya look at them speakers?!"

"I bet this thing plays real good!"

"You better be keepin' your eyes on that thing all the time, Miss Kremers, 'cause it's gonna get stole, just like everything else in this school! Look. All I have to do is climb up through that hole in the ceiling with my buddy and hide up there till everybody's gone. Then in the nighttime, come down and break that little ol' lock off the cupboard. Lower everything down through the window on ropes to the parking lot down there. Put it all in the truck I have waitin' on me – and be gone. It'd be easy! And nobody'd ever know who done it!"

"Tim's right, Miss Kremers. You watch. That bran' new stereo'll be gone in a week, and the speakers with it. You just wait and see."

The other miracle was the collection of pictures on the walls and bulletin board – the fact that they were there, on the walls and bulletin board, and not in shreds on the floor or altogether gone.

The first week of class, I had asked students to bring pictures, but they brought none. Maybe they didn't have any, or maybe they didn't want to attract attention. I brought some photos and put them up: Stevie Wonder, Herbie Hancock, Elton John, and some articles about their music. That was on a Wednesday. On Friday, everything was still there.

In time, other things appeared: two pictures of African Pygmies playing native instruments; Earlene's illustrated poem about a steel drum player; a news article about an African-American Hollywood star filming a movie at the Chicago inner-city high school he had attended; photos of how smoking affects the lungs; a fourteen-week-old fetus from the cover of Newsweek. Pictures spilled onto the walls: illustrations for a book the students wrote about musical instruments; pictures they drew with pastels as they listened to records. Even the tornado must have liked the idea, because every morning the pictures and the articles were still there.

As I closed the door to lock it, I thought about the piano, the only musical instrument we had. It was getting out of tune because students played it before and after class, but most of the keys still worked and the body was relatively unscarred. Whenever students pounded on the keyboard or stomped on the pedals, I yelled, "Hey! Treat it like an instrument!" And they did.

Front page, *Chicago Tribune,* September 15, 1974, "In Chicago, Teaching Defers to Survival":

The Chicago school system is almost too large for comprehension. It has a billion-dollar budget, a half-million students, 50,000 employees, and

611 buildings. Each year, 3,000 new teachers must be hired; each year, nearly one-third of all elementary school children change schools; each year, $2 million must be spent to repair broken windows; each year, 850 teachers report being physically assaulted; every day, 58,000 students are absent; every day there is a shortage of at least 200 substitutes.

🍎

"Is you the teacher?"

"How old you be?"

"Is you married?"

"You smoke reefer?"

"Can you bump?"

"Where your crib be located?"

"How come you ain't got no car?"

"What kinda music you teach, anyway?"

In 1974, one year of music was required by the Chicago Board of Education for high school graduation. Some Orr students auditioned for Band or Chorus, but most ended up in General Music, a course intended to teach music theory and history.

I was twenty-three. I had graduated from Stanford two years before, with degrees in English and Honors Humanities. I had moved to Chicago with my boyfriend, Brad, who was attending law school. After three frustrating months of working as a clerk at the Art Institute of Chicago, I had decided to get certified to teach English. I had attended the University of Illinois for two quarters, cramming in education courses and student teaching at Orr. Then, by some twist of fate, I had fallen into a fulltime job at Orr the following year. Not in English, though – in music.

During the first week of school, I gave my students a questionnaire. I could not have predicted their answers, particularly to the final question:

WHAT LIVE CONCERTS HAVE YOU BEEN TO, IF ANY?

Anthony: *No.*

Linda: *I was never to one.*

Mary Ann: *I've never been to any.*

Kerry: *No.*

Willie: *I haven't been to any not yet.*

Denise: *Never been to one.*

George: *I have not been to one.*

Orlander: *I have been to no concerts.*

Eddie: *None*

Beverly: *None*

Clifton: *I have never been to a live concert.*

Tim: *None.*

Sorin: *I haven't been to any concerts.*

Alfreda: *I have not been to a concerst.*

Greg: *I haven't been to any concerts in my whole life.*

Helen: *Yes. It was held in Sear Parking Lot.*

"Hey, Jerome! No radios in class, remember? Turn it off before you come in the room, or listen to it out in the hall... Thanks."

"Hey, Theresa! No food in class, remember? Put it away till later, or finish it out in the hall... Thanks."

"Hey, John! No dice in school! You better get rid of those quick! Put them in your pocket and keep them there!... Thanks."

"Hey, Tim! What have you got that knife out for? Well, if you need to sharpen your pencil, use the pencil sharpener in the library. I know it's a drag that there's no pencil sharpener in here. But you're not supposed to have knives in school, especially not switchblades… Thanks."

🍎

One snowy day in December I showed my four General Music classes a filmstrip about Johann Sebastian Bach. The filmstrip was narrated by a woman using simple language and was illustrated with color drawings. The students watched closely, and in the discussion afterward they were able to remember many facts.

I showed similar filmstrips about Mozart and Beethoven and brought tapes and records of medieval, renaissance, baroque, and classical music. I asked the students to close their eyes and let their minds wander with the sounds, to identify the instruments they heard, describe the moods, try conducting. After the first movement of Beethoven's fifth symphony – "Death Knocking at the Door," the students called it after seeing the filmstrip – I was surprised.

"Hey, that was neat! Play that again, Miss Kremers! C'mon, play it again!"

On the quiz over classical music, I asked the students to think about all of the periods of music history they had studied so far, to choose the one they liked best, and to give at least three reasons why.

The next day, I passed out copies of some of their answers.

"Orr students don't write like this!"

"You musta changed these around. Nobody in here know how to use commas and periods like this!"

"Look how long them answers is. Look at all them big words. Nobody at Orr writes this much!"

We listened to a few students read the answers out loud:

The kind of music I like is classical because it has more rhythm and more beat then the others cause what interested me was when the famous composers started off playing when they were so young. But the sad part was they didn't get much money for their work but they kept right on pushing like money was no big thing to them and didn't interest them at all but they loved their music and they kept right on pushing and until they had fame and to their death.

I like classical music because it sound's a little better than the music you here today, and it sends you off in two space it relax the mind.

I like to listen to classical music the best. Sometimes it helps me to relax when I am tired. It's nice to change the kind of music you hear once in a while. When you in a certain mood it helps to ease your problem away. When your tired of hearing popular music on the radio all day long it's nice to know that there's still radio stations you could listen too that have classical music on.

🍎

A few weeks later, Earlene, a stocky freshman with cocoa-colored skin and reddish hair, came early to class.

"Miss Kremers, how come we ain't got no suggestion box in this room? I think we should have one."

"That's a good idea, Earlene. What made you think of a suggestion box?"

"I saw it in a movie on TV the other night. *Up the Down Staircase.* It's about a school like ours, and they had a suggestion box. What if I brang one on Monday?"

"Great."

Earlene brought a dark green recipe box painted with pink

and white nail-polish flowers. There was a slit in the top and a handwritten sign taped to the front:

General Music	Ms. C. Kremer
Room 311	Periods 3, 4, 5, & 10
ORR Suggestion Box	

"What's that on your desk, Miss Kremers?"

"'ORR Suggestion Box.' What's that for?"

I asked the students if they had ever seen the movie *Up the Down Staircase.* Three or four in each class had seen it; the rest had never heard of it. I told them the movie was based on a novel, told by a white teacher who taught mostly black students in an inner-city high school like Orr, and that the school had problems similar to Orr's and even looked like Orr. I said that Earlene had brought the suggestion box after seeing the one in the movie. Then I told the students that they could write suggestions about anything – me, our class, themselves, life, anything, as long as they were respectful – and that they didn't have to sign their suggestions. The suggestions would be confidential, I would act on the ones I could, and perhaps we would discuss a few in class.

The students seemed enthusiastic, but in the month that followed, the box received only a handful of suggestions:

The girls in the room are ☐. Wear a dress. Why don't you change pants for a chance all you wear is Blue and brown.

I Hate test

I want the whole class to listen to records all day and no work.

I have such a hard time, because I'm lazy not physically, but when I say lazy I'm talking about using my head for something other than an head-rack. I guess I'm to hooked up in my imaginary world of my own. In grammar school things were easiler and I wished my highschool days would hurry and come, they did and now I hate it! I just can't adjest.

Earlene

You should have Thursdays as "Records day" when students bring their records to play at class people should bring rock soul & Latin music to listen and see which one is the best to listen to.

Teacher smiles to damn much. Works students to hard. Never likes have a good time, which once or twice a week. Doesn't give students a feeling of freedom in class room. Does not promote good morale. Has to much control over students.

Signed Sincerly Yours
Fuman Chu

I think you should start being the teacher. You have be a student to LONG! Letting the student do as they like, most of the time. Janice is always hollering and cursing about grades she receive, if she isn't holler-ing loud mouth Contrina is on the case, trying to stay in the right. You can't talk to a nigger without a little smartness in the conversation, let me repeat that to most negros. I'm a nergo and I know. So ethier start being the teacher or get out and let us!

From a concerned student!

I usually knew by the handwriting who had written a sugges-tion. One day I spoke with the person who had written "From a concerned student!"

"I read your suggestion about how you think Negroes should be spoken to, Earlene. I'm glad you wrote it. I know that many teachers here at Orr, black and white, do treat their students in an authoritarian way. With "smartness," as you call it. I'm not sure – maybe that is the best, most efficient way for them to act. But it seems to me a teacher shouldn't have to be a policeperson all the time, just because the students are black – or white, or whatever. A teacher ought to be able to act natural and the students ought to be able to act natural, too. It's a hard thing to do. Sometimes – like you said, with people like Janet or Katrina – it can backfire. It takes practice. But it seems to me it's worth trying."

Earlene said nothing. She was looking down at her shoes. She seemed to be listening, though. I decided to say more.

"A student like Janet makes a scene in our class sometimes because she's frustrated. She's failing almost every class she's in because she can't read. She cuts classes, gets in fights, gets suspended, skips tests, partly because she thinks she can't succeed anyway. Unless she's given some special attention, coaxed along, and allowed to vent her frustrations now and then, she won't make it in our music class, either. This takes patience – from the students, not just from the teacher. But it seems to me it could be worth it."

"You mean Janet can't read? She in high school and she can't read? I had no idea… No wonder…"

One day in January, after I had realized what Orr High School was mostly not about, I wrote some instructions on the chalk-board:

Today I challenge you to a contest.

1. Which class can list on the board the most names of musical instruments they hear on the records today?

2. Which class can keep me from saying any words the entire period?
The contest begins NOW. Good luck!

We had had Records Day every third Friday, after Harvey had put his suggestion in the box. Students brought rock and soul records and ran the stereo themselves, listing the songs and musicians on the board and sometimes identifying the instruments orally. Most students preferred just to listen to the music, though, and not to analyze it.

I had never tried running a class without talking. It seemed like a good experiment. Anyway, I had laryngitis that day and had realized, too late, that I should have stayed in bed. The school was an hour and a quarter's ride, by elevated train and bus, from the apartment on the North Side where Brad and I lived. After riding all that way, I didn't feel like turning around and riding back.

I sat down at one of the students' desks and waited.

"Hey, what you sittin' there for, Miss Kremers? You think you a student or somethin'?"

"'Today I chal-lenge you to a contest...' A contest! What kinda contest?"

"'... keep me from saying any words the entire period...' You mean you ain't gonna talk today? At all?!"

They figured it out.

"Hurry up! We gotta get started. Who's got the records? Here, I'll run the record player!"

"Shut the door, somebody!"

"Harvey, take that food outside! You knows you ain't spozed to have food in here! Take that outside, or Miss Kremers's gonna have to say somethin'!"

"What's she wavin' at us about? Oh, somebody's gotta write the names on the board! Here, I'll do it!"

"You can't spell worth nothin'! I'll do it!"

"No, I'm doin' it!"

"Hey, ya'll better stop yo' fightin', or Miss Kremers is gonna have to say somethin'! Take turns, why doncha?"

"I hear drums! Write down drums!"

"What's she wavin' about now?"

"I don't get it... Oh, what kinda drums! What kinda drums you hear, Willie?"

"Bass drum."

"And snare drum!"

"And bongos!"

"Erase those numbers, ya'll! We got three instruments there, not one!"

"Tambourine. I hear a tambourine!"

"How d'you spell it?"

"I don' know... "

"T-a-m... "

"Quiet, ya'll! I can't hear what he sayin'!"

"... b-o-... r-i-n?"

"No, that ain't right. Miss Kremers's shakin' her head that ain't right... Here, write down how to spell it on this piece o' paper, Miss Kremers!... There! T-a-m-b-o-u-r-i-n-e!"

"Piano!"

"That ain't no piano! That's a organ!"

"It's a piano!"

"Which is it, Miss Kremers?"

"She say it ain't neither one... "

"Oh, I know what it is! It's one o' them s... sy... You know what I mean!"

"Synthesizers!"

"Yeah, synthesizer!"

"How you spell synthesizer, Miss Kremers?"

It was a close race. Every class was able to keep me from saying a single word, and the winners came up with twenty-seven instruments, every one correctly spelled.

Front page, *Chicago Tribune*, September 14, 1975:

An Orr teacher, who asked that his name not be used, said the school was "a continuous riot from day to day. There's grass-smoking in the johns, and drinking and loitering in the halls. You find wine bottles around, and teachers and aides are subjected to all sorts of obscenities and threats."

Mike Royko, *Chicago Daily News*, April 5, 1974:

It's always fascinating to hear somebody who has an adventurous, dangerous job talk about hair-raising experiences. That's why I'm always willing to listen to the Chicago schoolteachers describe their latest thrills, chills, and spills.

I was talking to one the other day. She teaches at Orr High School, which is on the far West Side...

"You know, the gangs are recruiting again.... . It gets to be like a continual manhunt. Kids are running away, hiding out, staying home. There are stabbings and shootings...

"There are all kinds of weapons here. If you shook down every kid in

the building, you'd wind up with enough guns, knives, chains and things to have a small war...

"It's no wonder we're graduating illiterates. I mean illiterates. I had one senior who still couldn't get his name written correctly. I don't know how he'll ever fill out a job application when he can't get past his own name, but we gave him a diploma... ."

Chicago Daily News, April 16-17, 1975, "The Sound of Music in Chicago's Schools":

"...So, for the sake of perpetuating our musical heritage, and in the name of humanistic education, our children ought to go into the world knowing the names of Wolfgang Amadeus Mozart and Scott Joplin, as well as John Glenn and Richard J. Daley...."

The most popular music classes of the year, it turned out, were the ones when we studied the history of African-American music, in February. Those classes were also, for me, the most discouraging.

I showed a two-part filmstrip on the history and development of African-American music. The filmstrip began with the music of African tribes and moved through the music of slaves, spirituals, gospel, ragtime, minstrel shows, country blues, urban blues, modern blues, jazz, soul, opera singers, conductors, and concert pianists. Every person discussed was black.

The students loved it. They laughed at the "old-fashioned people," but they loved it. By the end, though, they could recall almost nothing.

Unlike the classical composer filmstrips that we had watched the first semester, these two filmstrips did not tell a chronological story, in simple language, of the life and music of a single person. These filmstrips presented a complex overview, in collage form, of the development of an entire culture's music. Dozens of names, faces, musical styles, and terms were presented that were completely new to the students, even though this was the history of their own music. They did not know how to spell the names they heard and they did not know how to use inventive spelling, so they could not write the names down. They had no way to capture, on paper, words like Underground Railroad, Scott Joplin, Billie Holiday, Louis Armstrong, Duke Ellington, Andre Watts.

The students were unable to recount anything – for instance, how slave songs had grown out of African tribal songs. Even when they watched that part of the filmstrip again, they had trouble answering questions about it and discussing it in their own words. They had spent nine, ten, eleven, twelve years in school, but they had not been taught how to learn. They could memorize facts that the teacher identified as important, and sometimes they could regurgitate them, and they could give their own previously formed opinions when asked. But most of them could not take a book, a newspaper article, a lecture, a television program, a filmstrip, or a movie and interact with it, except on the most superficial level. Even when it involved their own history.

I tried to imagine what it would be like to live in such darkness, but I could not. I could only wonder what the hell I was doing.

🍎

During the last week of March, before figuring report card

grades, I collected music notebooks in my four General Music classes. I had told the students the notebook needed to fulfill three requirements. It needed to be in a folder with holes and the papers threaded through the holes. It needed an illustrated title page. And it needed to be in some kind of order.

Although these were high school students, most did not know how to put a notebook together. For a cover, many used a tattered PeeChee with scribbles all over it. The students were not in the habit of saving homework, class notes, or quizzes. Once they saw their grades, they threw the papers away. If they did save papers, they didn't seem capable of categorizing them.

The previous semester, I had given my classes a list of categories to put their papers into and had told them to number all the pages and then to list the numbers in the table of contents. The project was a disaster. Students didn't know what a table of contents was, they didn't understand the categories, and they didn't number the pages or, if they did, they didn't understand how to list them in the table of contents. As for a title page, even though I described what a title page was and why it was needed, and showed them several examples in books, I got many notebooks with no title page, with the title page information scrawled on the notebook cover, or with a title page inside that said TITLE PAGE.

At first, I couldn't believe my eyes. Then I thought: if one had never considered how a book was put together, had never enjoyed reading a book, and perhaps had never been able to read a book, then one probably wouldn't know how to put together a book of one's own. The thing that incensed me was that these students were being passed on to tenth, eleventh, or twelfth grade - or were receiving diplomas - and most still did not know how to do basic academic tasks like assemble a notebook.

Earlene had turned in a notebook with numbered pages and several extra-credit sketches of musical instruments and of a group of classical musicians performing in an eighteenth-century drawing room. Harvey – seventeen years old, six feet five, attempting ninth grade for the second time – had failed the assignment in all three ways. I had often watched him copy my notes from the board, not word by word, but letter by letter.

Many of the notebooks, this second semester, fell in the middle. They showed a sense of organization and sparks of creativity, but they were riddled with problems in spelling, punctuation, and self-expression. The situation was epitomized by a paragraph written by Katrina, near the end of her notebook: *This is whats happing in Music at Orr high school I feel that my class is the best and the class is vere interesting and I enjoy my self. music is the past, present, and the future of the world, its whats happing. how music travle is vere interesting from ancient time down to the days kind of music. its amusicing how people change, when we except changes we except life and it includes music love makes the world go around and music helps it. people who made music famous are the happies people because thay are creative, thay used there mines.*

🍎

Harvey stood by the stereo, about to play the first side of the record he had brought. All the lights had been turned off. Janet had written the name of the album on the chalkboard and was listing underneath it the songs on the first side.

Usually on Records Day, students brought stacks of 45s with

the latest AM soul hits, since not many students owned albums. A few times, though, Willie had brought his well-worn *Headhunters* album by Herbie Hancock, and once Winfred brought his *Skin-Tight* album by the Ohio Players. Today, the only person to bring a record was Harvey. One brand-new album. The music began.

It was *Elton John's Greatest Hits,* recorded between 1970 and 1974. This was the first time someone had brought a folk-rock record. Usually students brought soul or, sometimes, jazz.

I knew that Elton John was a white singer and a keyboard play-er, but I did not know many of his songs. I sat in my chair in the semi-darkness and watched the faces before me: twenty-five black ones, two Latino, two white.

I will never forget the scene that followed.

Many students knew the lyrics to "Goodbye Yellow Brick Road," "Your Song," "Don't Let the Sun Go Down on Me" – and their lips moved silently with the music. Some rested their heads on their desks, some did homework, some stared into space. And some looked directly at me.

Arranged before me in the dark, as if captured in the stop-action lens of a black-and-white camera, were twenty-nine people with whom I had shared forty minutes every day for the last 133 days. Outside our classroom door were two thousand more peo-ple like them, outside our school were tens of thousands more, and outside our city in other cities, millions. Rows and rows of people born into less fortunate circumstances than I, smothering in institutions like this. The words on the record seemed to grow louder and louder. "Don't let the sun go down on me / Don't let the sun…"

One week later, I left Orr High School. I could not continue to work at a place and a task I did not believe in.

I had done my best to make my actions as a teacher consistent with my beliefs in relevant, humanistic education. But I did not feel that my isolated efforts were making a difference in my students' lives. To them, I was just one of five or six alien figures with whom they spent a small part of every day. Perhaps, I thought, I could do more by writing about them than by teaching.

I gave a letter of resignation to the principal and asked the students to complete another questionnaire. It was April 1975. They wished me well. Katrina scrawled at the bottom: *I just hope you remember us at Orr High School...*

Twenty years and probably two thousand students later, I still remember Orr High School. That's because, of course, its problems exist everywhere. My culture, the dominant culture, the Anglo-European culture, continues to feed non-white students with white teachers, white values, and white goals. What gets eaten up stems from there.

If I focused on that – on all that damage, on all that misunderstanding and loss – I would have given up for good that day in April when I wrote to Kenneth van Spanckeren, a sandy-haired Dutch man, the school's new principal, about why I could not continue to teach in his school. But Ken van Spanckeren is a fine man and a fine principal, I understand, and the last I heard – in 1986, when I telephoned to ask the Orr school secretary to sign a form for me – "Mr. V" was still there.

Yes, I hate schools. What I hate most about them is their ability to reduce creative individuals to a mixed-up mass.

I remember inventing tunes on the ebony and chipped ivory keys of the piano at home, when I was four. I would go into the den and close the door, climb up on the wooden stool at the dusty piano, and experiment. This was very much fun. Sounds came out that I liked and didn't like, and I tried to remember the ones I liked and play them again. I played the sequence over and over, until I had a tune. Then I played the tune every day, so I wouldn't forget it.

Who taught me this? Why did it give me so much pleasure? And why was I unable to sustain this ability and joy as I grew into a schoolchild and an adolescent, a young woman and a lover, an adult and a wind-tossed sail?

The fact that the medium, later, became words instead of music – the music of words and the application of the music of words to human problems – is still a source of wonder and mystery to me. I did not learn to do any of this solely in school. In fact, often, I learned it in spite of school.

I would not teach today at Orr what I taught twenty years ago. I would throw out the curriculum – secretly, if necessary – and teach what I thought the students really needed. I hate schools. Yet, I cannot condemn Orr High School for the time wasted, the spontaneity and creative energy snuffed out. This is the nature of schools. I have also seen students learn, seen interests sparked and opportunities provided that the students would not have had otherwise.

I hate schools, but I love to teach.

BEVERLY A. BUNCHER

A Teachable Moment

Context is everything. So, when one of my journalism students asked his tablemates, "Is anyone here Jewish?" I didn't respond right away. "Because if not, I have a great Jewish joke to tell..."

I wanted to know why he, an Asian American, wanted to know. It didn't take long to find out.

Hearing my student's words brought back memories. Of course, by age 40, I'd heard my share of anti-Semitic slurs.

At 26, I worked at a business school in Pittsburgh and overheard two Caucasian students whispering and laughing out loud. The only audible words were "Jewish" and "kike."

On our honeymoon in Hawaii a woman at the front of our tour bus suddenly began yelling about "dirty Jews." I'll never forget my husband's response: "You better watch it lady; we Jews back here don't like what you're saying." She shut up instantly.

During the Gulf War, I was teaching in a Virginia public school. One day, I found swastikas drawn in my roll book and on my desk. Later, I found a large one scratched into my chalk-board. The chalkboard was replaced.

Soon after, I saw a Jewish colleague crying in the hallway. An adolescent student told her he wished Hitler had finished the job. That same year a teen in my classroom said something endearing about Hitler. The administration's consistent response was, "They're kids. Kids will be kids."

Words. They were, after all, just words. But throughout the history of my family and my people, words too often have led to action. Like the time my great-grandfather was captured by Polish soldiers, just because he was Jewish. They beat him, shaved off the beard that distinguished him as an observant Jew, and jailed him for 24 hours, just because... When he got out of jail, the family pooled its money and sent him to the U.S., where he worked until he could send for everyone else.

History and my grandmother taught me that not everyone was so lucky. I have visions of her sitting at her kitchen table in Pittsburgh throughout the 1920's and early thirties, savoring every word in each letter she received from her cousins, aunts, and uncles left behind in the old country. Then, as Hitler's plan unfolded, the letters stopped coming – one by one. And there she sat, at her kitchen table, waiting for word of their survival. Finally, in the late forties, a cousin wrote from Israel, an uncle from Argentina, and a niece from California. They'd made it out somehow, but what about the scores of others in our family?

I can still see my grandmother telling me that story. Seated at the same rectangular table, with its white plastic tablecloth, she dusted crumbs off the table as she recounted each loss, each letter that no longer came. It seemed to me, as a young girl, that each crumb traveling from table to floor represented another lost relative.

🍎

These memories made me sensitive to the power of ethnic slurs. So when one of my students sat in my classroom preparing a group of his friends to participate in some "ethnic humor," I had to respond.

"I'm Jewish," I said, "and your words hurt. If I heard a joke about Asians, I wouldn't repeat it – whether any Asians were present or not."

He stopped to look at me with jaw dropped and eyes open wide. "I..."

A stillness came over the classroom.

Context truly is everything. After a moment or two in the silence, I proceeded with the lesson, which, coincidentally enough, was "How to write life-changing articles." So, I introduced the topic and asked the students to brainstorm a list of subjects they would find meaningful and interesting to read or write about.

As they did so, I took out a piece of easel paper, taped it to the board and began writing this very article as a model. When I finished the first draft, I shared it aloud with my students.

"Any moment, in school or out, can lead to an article filled with life-changing information," I said. The bell rang before I could finish reading the article aloud. Everyone walked out except for the boy who inspired the story. He stayed behind and walked up to me, eyes wet, head down.

"I'm sorry," he managed to say. "I guess I didn't think before I opened my mouth."

"It's a cruel world," I said softly. "We humans have to stick together."

"I know you're right," he said.

Rubbing the tears from his eyes, he walked over to the board, read the rest of the article, and walked out the door. I rubbed the tears from my eyes as my next class walked in.

A week later, I showed him the second draft.

"Would you mind if I published it?" I asked.

Tears filled his eyes as he read it again. Silently, I awaited his response.

"It's an important article," he said. "In civics, we are learning about the importance of doing things for the 'common good' and I think this could be one of those things."

If racism occurs on a continuum, and context is everything, then maybe this young man had made a step toward becoming less racist, and we had shared what we in education call "a teachable moment."

MICHAEL O'ROURKE

excerpted from "Teachers"
A Brightly-Lit Room

I took Professor Walters my senior year, final term. The course was The American Novel: 1914-39, a course like no other I had yet taken. Part of it was Walters himself – a brash, egotistical, brilliant lecturer who knew he was brilliant, chain-smoking his way through every class. He'd get mad at us for not "participating" more, for not speaking up, but his intellect was so imposing that I, for my part, just wanted to listen to him. Here's the class that turned me around:

He assigns *The Sun Also Rises,* and when we get to class, he announces that today it's just Chapter One. First surprise: Not the whole novel? Not half of it? Just the first chapter? It's only five pages long. How can we spend a whole class on one chapter?

Walters wants to know about Cohn's nose. It was flattened in a boxing match, which "*gave him a certain satisfaction of some strange sort.*"

"What's this satisfaction? What's Hemingway, through Barnes, telling us about Cohn?"

We peer at our books for the answer.

"What's the insinuation? He doesn't come right out and say it, but what's he suggesting?"

Well, he's Jewish, but that can't be it. Must be something "deeper." I raise my hand (and here, dear reader, is where I prove to you my willingness to strip myself bare):

"Is it a phallic symbol?"

Walters laughs uproariously.

"Who told you that? Does someone in this department teach phallic symbols? Who? Tell me who."

Well, yes, someone does, and I took him for two classes. I thought he was pretty good, but I sit mum.

"Look, it's probably racist on Hemingway's part, but Cohn's Jewish, and he's glad his nose was flattened because it makes him look less Jewish, it makes him look more Gentile. He's this insecure little wimp, and he doesn't want to stand out; he wants to look like everyone else."

Oh.

Next, Walters singles out two words: "took to." *"In his last year at Princeton he read too much and took to wearing spectacles."*

"Hemingway, at his best, is a very careful writer. He uses words sparingly. He tells us things without saying them. What's he telling us about Cohn when he says Cohn *took* to wearing spectacles?"

Well, that he started wearing them. He read too much, so he had to start wearing glasses. Something beyond that? Something "deeper"? Sight...vision...lack of vision...whose eyes were put out?...Cyclops, one eye...

"It's an affectation! He didn't start wearing spectacles, he took to wearing them. Barnes doesn't think he really needed them. He took to wearing them because he thought they made him look more thoughtful or something. *Read the words.*"

Oh.

Walters has us flip to the third page where Cohn *"had been taken in by a lady who hoped to rise with the magazine Cohn had started.*

"Then Hemingway keeps on using the word *lady* in that paragraph. Never even gives us her name until the next paragraph, but then goes back to *lady. Lady* over and over. Why?"

Well, she's a woman, so...But by now I'm lost, and no one's saying a word. I stare uncomprehendingly at the paragraph.

"She's not a lady, she's a *bitch!* He basically tells us that in lots of other ways. He keeps calling her "lady" over and over to underscore the fact that she's not a lady. It's like Antonius in *Julius Caesar* when he keeps calling Brutus an *honorable* man. The more he says honorable the more we hear *scum.*"

Of course. Why didn't I see that? What's wrong with me? Why am I not getting this?

Walters backs up, makes some other points, then jumps to the newspaper. At the end of the chapter, Barnes, Cohn, and Cohn's "lady" finish their drinks, Barnes is leaving, and *"Cohn said he wanted to buy a paper and would walk to the corner with me,"* after which follows their conversation about Cohn's woman and their trip.

"What is it with this newspaper? It's just a detail, but why is it there? How does it function in the scene? Near the end of the scene Barnes comes back to the newspaper. He says Cohn *'turned with the paper in his hand,'* and in the next to the last sentence he's *'holding his paper.'* Before that he reminds Cohn that he forgot to get his paper. What's with the paper?"

Writing...journalism...literature...Cohn had started that magazine...

"It's Cohn's *excuse!* He's so afraid of his lady, he's so damned *hen-pecked,* that he has to have an excuse to get away from her for two minutes so he can talk with Barnes in private. And Barnes knows that, he sees that. He even has to remind Cohn to get his paper. Look. You people need to learn how to read. You're senior English majors. What's going on? You look right past what's on the page, and strain for something that isn't there. And in the process you miss the subtleties that are there. There's nothing 'deep and dark' about that paper, for instance, but it does play a role in the scene, and you missed that role. *Read the words.* Class dismissed."

🍎

That's a reconstruction, of course, and I had help from my tattered copy of *The Sun Also Rises* in which I found my dutiful markings of the points we "discussed," but the light bulbs were clicking on so fast that day that "Chapter One" is forever a brightly-lit room. And in a sense it was chapter one, first grade all over again.

PRISCILLA LONG

Too Late for Miss Roselli

I once had visions of becoming one of the Great Minds of the West. This was at Moravian Seminary for Girls in Bethlehem, Pennsylvania in the late 1950s. At Moravian Seminary we wore uniforms with white anklets and saddle shoes. We attended chapel every morning, and we also prayed before breakfast, dinner, and study hall. In our 11th grade history class taught by Miss Fanny Roselli, we were studying the French Revolution.

It was exciting becoming one of the Great Minds of the West. I would go to the library, an oak-paneled room lined with books and fitted out with refectory tables. I would spend an hour puzzling through two or three paragraphs of Hegel in one of the *Great Books of the Western World* – I intended to read each of the Great Books.

The librarian, Miss Hartman, had never known another Moravian Seminary girl to do such a thing, and she liked me. I was drawn to thick books. I would read them and keep score, rather like counting laps in a swimming competition. At 17, I had long since read *War and Peace* (1,483 pages). I had read *Les*

Miserables (1,463 pages), *The Hunchback of Notre Dame* (688 pages), and *The Three Musketeers* (555 pages). Miss Hartman encouraged me to read books based on factors other than number of pages. I read every book she suggested, including *The Bridge Over the River Kwai, Archie and Mehitable,* and *Till We Have Faces.*

In our history class, the unit on the French Revolution was especially exciting. I looked upon our textbook with scorn, and I didn't read it. With happy anticipation, I tackled both Edmond Burke's *Reflections on the Revolution in France,* and Thomas Carlyle's three-volume *History of the French Revolution.* Carlyle was thrilling! Of some desperate finance minister he wrote, "What could a poor minister do? A sinking pilot will fling out all things, his very biscuit bags, lead, log, compass and quadrant, before flinging out himself. It is on this principle of sinking, and the incipient delirium of despair, that we explain likewise the almost miraculous 'Invitation to Thinkers.'" And so on.

Already I had made July 14 – the day the Mob liberated the Bastille – my own personal holiday. I made *Liberte, Egalite, Fraternite* my own personal motto. I believed every word of the Declaration of the Rights of Man. I could almost feel the cold blade of the guillotine on the hot neck of Marie Antoinette.

I arrived at class each day full of excitement and often raised my hand to offer a comment or to answer a question. I was Miss Roselli's favorite 11th grade girl, I was fairly certain.

I fancied myself a thinker.

The day of the test arrived. I entered the old wood-floored classroom filled with a sense of expectation of impending triumph. On the test I wrote and wrote, pouring myself fourth on the French Revolution. I finished with a feeling of pride, imagining how pleased and possibly even excited Miss Roselli would be.

The next day we were to get back our test. We entered the classroom and took our seats, fifteen girls wearing pastel uniforms with round white collars, white anklets and white-and-brown saddle shoes. Miss Roselli entered. The girls stood. Miss Roselli said, "You may be seated." The girls sat and folded their hands on their desks. Miss Roselli put her briefcase on the desk and drew out the tests. The class waited in silent anticipation. Without a word, Miss Roselli went from desk to desk, returning the tests.

I looked at my test. I could not believe my eyes. On the test Miss Roselli had drawn a large red F. I was in shock. I kept looking at it to make sure it was really an F. I turned the test over to see if there was a mistake. Then I turned it back to the front. Miss Roselli had written a single comment next to the F: "How can you write about the French Revolution without mentioning Voltaire?" Voltaire. I had forgotten Voltaire.

Miss Roselli was speaking to the class. She was a small-boned woman with straight black and gray hair, which she parted on one side and barretted on the other. She had a thin mouth and pale papery skin and she wore granny glasses and idolized Arnold Toynbee. Now she was talking on and on about something, but I did not hear her. When the bell rang, I rose and trooped out of the classroom along with the other girls. I did not look at Miss Roselli, nor did I speak to her.

I stopped reading books on the French Revolution. Instead, I memorized the textbook. The next test was a true/false test, and I answered all the questions correctly. I finished the question twenty minutes before the end of the class and sat among the busy test-takers with my hands folded on my desk, in scornful silence. On that test, I got an A.

So that proved it. The conventional ones, the little minds, the obedient ones, the ones that studied for grades and learned by rote, the ones that couldn't care less about the French Revolution, or about Hegel or about Tolstoy, they were the ones who got the stamp of approval. I proved to Miss Roselli that I could do that too, if I wanted to. But it was beneath me, and it was too late for Miss Roselli.

I never spoke to her again.

CHAPTER FOUR

Between the Lines

There is nothing more inspiring than
having a mind unfold before you.

—ABRAHAM KAPLAN

BENJAMIN GROSSBERG

For Beth

All semester you have been writing – poems, stories,
even a short play, each a variation on the same
text, each poem the same song despite differences
in form and action, each story telling the same story:
whether the protagonist is a man or a woman, crazy
(a psychopath, you said) in one, a veteran (it doesn't matter
which war) in another. This is what you have to tell –
to me? I wonder, who reads with a felt tip,
doles checks and asterisks with the liberal hand
of praise, brackets judiciously to suggest
greater lyric consideration. No, not to me. I am only
a formality in the person of myself, an audience
standing in for all audience, perhaps in whom,
through whom, you strive to tell yourself.

Beth, this repetitive gesture you enact,
it is the hand sweep of an eastern art of movement,
the way I grab a lock of hair when thinking, and pulse,

it is the shivering and bobbing of prayer under
a white and blue shawl; do you know that?

This hand sweep of detail, davening of diction,
wailing at the old stone wall of your misfortune,
these details you share only in intense intimacy
with your page, and somehow with me: *the first time*
during a Christmas party. Beth, I shouldn't
know this about you. I *could hear my mother*
laughing downstairs. Do you hear how your detail
reassembles, recombines like fragments of DNA
in an attempt to formulate a healed woman? *And then*
he started moving faster and closed his palm
over my mouth. I comment diligently
in the margins: what fine lineation you use;
I admire the poem's courage. Here
The details are especially immediate –
here, where you describe the feel
of his belt buckle, here the felt sense of dead
weight. I can say nothing useful –

The violation, the battering of a dozen figures,
lyric speaker, dramatic monologue, and the true
story of a Vet who raped and killed a small boy
for stealing his radio – all is lost by the proper
distance between student and teacher. Even a gesture
of feeling would be too intimate, would break
the fourth wall and acknowledge to the audience
that I am only an actor playing this old man's part,
that I stand silent behind the arras waiting for my cue

to die; the person behind this teacher, the person
behind you, the student, and then the speaker
that you have created – on some almost lost
level, Beth, we must still be two humans
interacting, negotiating over a cauldron of loss:
and there it is not witches' brew, no stage
machination, but the disease that fashions
even the most privileged, and the work
involved sharing any depth of pain.

What I would write on your text – in another
context – on all your texts, what I would tell you
about how these images may animate in your mind
like a flip book, for the rest of your life,
how they may follow you into and out of
waking, peek around a doorway like a child,
when you begin to walk toward the door of sleep,
how they may thicken the ink in your pen –
and how it may to some degree be so
with all of us, that a tiny kernel of loss
pulls out again and again, is ripped
from the inside to brilliant whiteness
by shaking movement and heat, and the inside
flowers out – what I would say to you....

Maybe I would remind you of the day we walked
away from Main Hall, late autumn, the leaves
blowing across the road in front of us.
You looked at me with a guileless smile and said,
"that one, the Christmas poem, is about me."

Maybe I would remind you how I retreated
behind my jargon, praised the shape of your lyric,
the arc of your project this semester, how deeply
it struck me – and then how I walked away
aware that I had just committed a terrible act
of safety, and that no doubt I was not
the first person in your life who had
the feelings I had for you, Beth, the knowledge
I let drift along with the blowing leaves
until it too became undifferentiated and lost
on the college lawn – that something, something
important that you had just said, had been heard.

Barbara A. Rouillard

Callers

When my husband, William, and I bought a house and moved, we had some decisions to make. Since we do not share the same last name, we had to determine whose name would be listed in the phone book with our new telephone number.

"Put the listing in your name," William instructed me.

"OK." I looked over at William.

"You know," he continued. "In case they need you." I knew William was thinking of Tim.

It is late, past midnight, when something pierces my slumber. I open my eyes to see William's face within inches of mine. He's whispering something. Something about someone being here. Something about someone having died.

I sit up. William pokes my arms into the sleeves of my bathrobe. I stand and look at myself in the mirror. I am reluctant to go out there. What is lurking on the other side of this bedroom door? I hear William ask, "Do you need a few moments to compose yourself?"

"No." I belt my robe. I open the door a crack, peek around the corner and see Tim standing in the middle of our living room carpet.

Now I see from the clock that hangs over our bookcase that it's past one in the morning. Tim stands rigid, with tears pouring down his face.

"Timmy died tonight, about two hours ago," he blurts out.

My "oh, no," is sincere. We sit down at the table. Just waking, I am hesitant to speak; I don't want to say anything wrong or hurtful to this student of mine from ten, twelve years ago. His son has just died, and somehow I can feel Timmy in the air around us.

I finally ask, "How old was Timmy?"

"Five."

"Did he ever speak or hear?"

"No."

"Did he ever eat or drink anything?"

"No, just from the tube in his stomach." I look over and see that William has taken a seat beside us at the table.

"What happened, Tim? How did Timmy die?"

"He stopped breathing," Tim cries out. "Because he couldn't walk, his lungs filled up." William sits watching the two of us.

I fill in William by asking Tim to "please tell Bill how long the doctors expected Timmy to live when he was born."

"Five days," Tim answers. Five days and tonight Timmy dies at the age of five years.

"Tim, what happened tonight?" I repeat my question.

"The doctors told me today, actually yesterday now," as he looks at the clock, "that Timmy was dying, so I took him home. I wanted him to die at home. When I told Timmy that he could leave now, he died within twenty minutes."

I believe Tim. "Tim," I tell him. "Did you know how amazed I was five years ago when you came to my classroom to show me Timmy? How much I admired you? I have to tell you the truth; I don't have your gifts, I would have let the baby die in the hospital."

"No, you wouldn't have."

"Yes, I would have. Jenny felt the same way. After you left that day, Jenny and I couldn't believe what a natural you were. We so admired your love for your child. We were especially impressed by how you didn't act like Timmy was your cross to bear." Jenny was another teacher at the school.

"I didn't think of him as a cross to bear," Tim answers.

"I know."

Tim smiles through his tears. "You know," he says, "once a priest asked me how I would change Timmy if I could, and I answered, 'Nothing. There is nothing I would change about Timmy,' and I wouldn't have. I couldn't picture Timmy any way else, right from the beginning." And as Tim is speaking, I picture Timmy at a wedding two years ago. Timmy in a miniature tuxedo in an oversized wheelchair with tubes and diapers.

"Why did he have to die so young?" Tim cries.

I grasp for answers. After all, I was Tim's teacher, and he's come here. "Tim," I finally answer, "I have a theory, probably more of a belief. You know how they say the good die young?"

Tim nods his head.

"Well, maybe Timmy's life was so short because maybe he had only small lessons to learn. Maybe, in the next life Timmy will be healthy or maybe we'll be as healthy as Timmy is."

Tim laughs, then cries out, "You may not understand this, because I have a wife and a job and a daughter, but now that Timmy is gone, what am I going to do? I mean, I have nothing to do now."

I smile. "Tim, I do understand. The morning after our dad died, after a long bout with cancer, I went to my divorced sister's house, and there she was crying in the middle of her totally trashed living room with two preschoolers at her knees. She cried out, just like you, 'Barbara, what am I going to do now? I have nothing to do now.'"

"You do understand." Yes.

At four, Tim leaves. William and I go to bed.

"I didn't know what to do when this young guy showed up at the door and rang our buzzer," William tells me. "He wanted to see you, but I didn't know what to do until he started to cry. You must have made quite an impression on him," William continues.

"No," I answer. "He made quite an impression on me." I lean over, kiss William good night, and turn off the light with the feeling Timmy is somewhere between our home and his father's.

"Put the phone listing under Rouillard," William told me." In case one of the kids ever needs to find you."

REBECCA J. KAISER

Breakable Ashley

Mr. Smith said Ashley was brittle.

Oh my God, I thought. Peanut brittle. You never find a piece that's not broken.

"William feels entitled."

Crap. Entitled to what? I should know but I don't. Oh, my God...am I ever screwed. Thirty days earlier I quit my secure, tenured job, to work with these kids who'd been kicked out of regular school.

"Arica: statuesque."

"T'Shad: a late bloomer."

"David: a loner."

"Tracey: pedantic."

Only one thing was sure. The next day, waiting for breakable Ashley, Mr. Smith would leave, and I would be new.

Classes were delayed on my first day at this strange alternative school – to make time for the community police. They had come every Thursday since September, I was told, with a speaker or videotape. Something like that. That first day they brought four members of Narcotics Anonymous. Several classes gathered in my room for the meeting.

Most of the seats were empty, at first. I was frantically looking for clues about kids, listening for names, trying to get a feel for how this place worked. Every few minutes another student would walk in, find a seat in the circle, bang a chair, forget to say "excuse me." Black. White. Hispanic. Clean. Dirty. Baby faces and criminal types. They looked at their shoes, and some tried to sleep. A few kept asking to leave. I counted them nervously...twenty-five, twenty-six. In college, I had a job as a lifeguard where I counted heads in the water all day long. Just like this.

The meeting was supposed to last an hour. But the students, one after the other, kept asking questions. I thought they were dragging it out to avoid going to class until I realized the members of Narcotics Anonymous were allowing the questions to continue because they thought the questions were good.

An hour and a half had gone by when, suddenly, the outside door, down the hallway, banged shut. A girl dashed in, hair pulled back in a tight rubber band. She looked athletic – and mean. A young teacher whom I didn't know got up and stood behind her now-empty chair.

"Ashley," she motioned, "Sit here."

So this was breakable Ashley, I thought.

The girl flopped down sideways, turning her back to the speaker, a nasty scowl on her face. Then the young teacher reached down and stroked Ashley's hair. Twice. Very gently. From her forehead all the way back to her ponytail. Ashley's face mellowed. She became beautiful, like the innermost part of herself.

Hope, I thought, might be found in this place.

JEFFREY LEE

A Little Hopeful

In 1995, the city of Camden had the highest murder rate per capita in the country. A young mother in tears struggled to explain to me in my office: "My ex- my – I mean, my separated husband – is threatening to take my children away."

I had seen her daughter once and remembered her big blue lollipop, her deep blue tongue, and her eyes, so big and empty, like pools of rainwater waiting for the sunlight to come back. She was so patient when her mother came for extra help.

The mother was crying because of the stress of worrying about final exams and her minimum wage job and the day care her kids were in. She was afraid she wouldn't do well in the class. I told her, "You're doing fine – just keep going ahead the same way you have been."

She said, "He has been stalking me – I can't relax unless I'm doing something." Then she explained all the safety precautions she continually had to take.

I said, "Maybe the studying could help you forget about your worries. Study time could be like another place, a hiding place."

"He is so determined," she said, "He fought his former wife so hard. He hurt her a lot."

Then she explained in detail about his relentless tactics.

"Are you safe where you are now?"

"I think so – except when I have to go to work or school," she said.

But that was almost all of the time.

By far the worst shame for her was having to go on welfare to get medical coverage for her daughters. She had no coverage at work for anything, despite working full-time (and the money was actually less than welfare, which had benefits). I told her I had a student with kids who went on welfare while in college but then got a good job. She looked a little hopeful and stopped crying.

Six months later another woman student looked terribly dejected all through the Saturday morning class. She was so obviously unhappy I wondered what was wrong.

During break she said, "I have to tell you something – in private."

Off we went to the bookstore, and on the way down the three flights of stairs she said, "I'm afraid of my husband coming to class. He's been threatening me. He says he knows where he can find me. He could show up any day."

She explained the whole situation bit by bit – it was bad: "He won't get help, but he made promises to..."

We had coffee outside the little bookstore, and she continued. "He started beating me recently. I said to myself, 'I won't tolerate this – I'm not that kind – I got self-respect.'" She explained how she left, or tried to, but he started stalking her. She gave me a complete description, and we went to tell campus security about him.

"He's stocky and strong, about 200 pounds – he works as a security guard."

He had just that week beaten her and ground his knee into her head against the floor, so that she had to go to the doctor and the dentist. The flesh over her cheekbone was still bruised badly under a thick layer of make-up. He had rocked his whole body weight over her to crush her face. Her neck was still sore. It explained her smoldering misery in class. Then she started to cry over her coffee and told me what she could do and what she couldn't do.

Worried about how she might feel if pushed in any direction, I gave no advice. I only listened carefully and said, "I hope you can escape."

She disappeared for three weeks and turned up with a withdraw slip. She told me that her divorce lawyer was too willing to drop charges against her husband because he made countercharges. This lawyer seemed to be concerned mainly with getting as much money for as little work as possible. She wanted a new lawyer who would press her case the way it should go. But since she had so little money, this lawyer didn't care what she wanted.

Knowing how futile her situation was, I said only, "I hope things can work out for you somehow." She had a badly swollen lower jaw – I don't ask. She told me she had a safe place to stay with her sister, whose husband was with the police. That sounded solid.

I have never been trained to help people like this.

Another afternoon the phone rang, and one of the women in my evening class said in a slow, shaky voice, "This is Darlene from your Wednesday night class, Professor."

I already knew it was terrible news as I said, "Yes. I remember you."

Then she apologized for having been in a car crash on Route 38. A van slammed into her car from behind and gave her severe whiplash; she and her two-year-old daughter were in the car. She asked, "Can I bring my papers in next week?"

"That's on time anyway, actually. And if you need an extra week, that's fine."

Once I got a phone call from the mother of one of my favorite students who had been absent four classes in a row, inexplicably. I started to sweat because I had already started to worry. She said he was in a car crash and was in Cooper Trauma Unit.

"I hope he gets better soon," I said, suddenly unhappy. I asked her what to do regarding his schoolwork, "Is there any chance he will come back?"

She said, "No," but thanked me as though she were really grateful.

That same month, the worst student in all of my classes showed up early for class one day with panic in his eyes. I already knew he was going to give me an excuse, but I was really surprised when he said, "Professor, I gotta go with the police tuh splain I'm not guilty. They waitin' for me outside. So I can't turn in my paper."

It took a moment for me to digest this. I knew he was being perfectly honest. "What happened?"

"I was *innocent*. I was just in the car with these other four guys, and they got picked up for some disturbances."

"You got picked up too?"

"Uh huh."

"What do you mean by 'disturbances'?"

He started a tongue-tied, rambling sentence about some parking lot vandalism that he and his friends only witnessed.

"Okay, let me know what happens. Don't just disappear."

He disappeared for weeks. When he came back, exonerated, he wanted to withdraw. I knew he would sooner or later. Sometimes I just got this feeling from young ones who were too overwhelmed to pursue anything higher. But in his own way, he was sincerely trying. It was the best he could do then.

One semester my best student out of all five classes (which included four composition sections of twenty-five students) was in the same class as the worst. Nonetheless, the best student won the Holcombe Writing Award. She deserved it, and I was really happy for her – it was $250 for writing the best essay selected from the college-wide competition. At last – something to celebrate!

The very same week I got a polite rejection from Oxford

University Press on a book proposal. I blamed myself for not working harder – but I thought how little time I had had to do a decent job on a truly worthy project. Who could contemplate William and Dorothy Wordsworth of 1798 in Grasmere, England, while laboring over hundreds of mostly mediocre essays in Camden in 1996?

I feared that education was like a life preserver with too many desperate hands trying to hold on, and that we were laborers in a triage economy where more and more people sink into poverty so deep no one can teach or help them.

Another working day ended. Another working night began. I was concerned because one of the best students in my 8:00 class in Women's Literature has been out for three weeks. I didn't want to imagine... He said he was a poet, and he had that look about him. He was a former merchant marine and capable of penetrating, ironic wit. He wrote brilliantly about Christina Rossetti. But he never came back.

That year I also lost two students to cancer.

In general, the average Camden student was twenty-eight, worked full-time and was a full-time student. Many had children – and their wages were often even lower than ours. Yet I doubted many of them earned less than the adjunct professors, who bore the brunt of our labor. All of us worked so hard for so little that one had to think very hard before making judgments about anyone there.

One academic year I was blessed by an offer to be a Visiting Assistant Professor at Franklin & Marshall College in Lancaster, Pennsylvania, a city amid beautiful Amish country. I was released from Camden for a year to write and do research. The teaching load here was only five courses *per year*, and they paid more. My students were eighteen or nineteen; they worked part-time campus jobs – if they worked. They were frequently brilliant, always hardworking, and wonderfully respectful. I heard just one tragic story and one distressed complaint – a student wailed loudly because she failed to get into choir.

I explained to one professor who asked about Camden that the campus in the suburbs had most of the Caucasians; meanwhile, the city campus had most of the African-Americans, Chicanos, Asian-Americans and all those designated as "Other."

He seemed startled, "That's *de facto* segregation."

"Yes, it is. I'm afraid many of my students at Camden were blatantly prejudiced. Some didn't even realize it would seem wrong to me. The irony was that they were so much alike though they thought of themselves as in different worlds. They all worked inhuman hours. And regardless of race, they were mostly conservative on social issues like capital punishment."

The professor didn't reply.

🍎

One Camden student, an Army veteran of the Gulf War, tried so hard to study, raise a son and work full-time. "But there aren't any good jobs blowing things up," he explained.

We'd been reading the Harlem Renaissance poets and later African-Americans, and he loved them. Then he was gone for weeks and returned one day to withdraw.

Clutching his own second-hand paperback of African-American literature, he was so grateful. "You opened my eyes. I want to thank you. We were never taught *any* of this in high school! I realize now – I was robbed."

He looked me in the eye, smiled warmly and was gone.

MELINDA STILES

Filed but Not Forgotten

Each August many new students come to us with warning labels. The long list of students and their ailments – allergies and illnesses – is handed out the first day. We highlight the names of students we have in class and file the list away.

One Monday, five days before semester's end, my seniors began delivering their final exam speeches. I sat in the center row, last seat, to evaluate them. Jason sat sideways in the desk in front of me and placed one arm on my desk. He was a mainstreamed special ed. student, painfully shy, who agonized through every minute of the required speech class.

Jason didn't look at the speakers. He stared at my paper as I wrote the evaluations. I was mildly irritated by his scrutiny but didn't say anything. If this attentiveness meant he was coming out of his shell, I didn't want him to retract.

During one speech a movement on my desk caught my eye. Jason's hand was stiff and a single finger twitched. A fleeting recollection. Jason's name on the warning list. A millisecond of fear flitted through my body. Jason's head fell back. His legs twitched. No time for fear.

I stood up. "Jason is having a seizure. Help me get him to the floor. Move the desks away from him."

Trevor and Mark lifted Jason to the floor. Everyone pushed desks out of the way.

Trevor took off his new jacket of which he was so proud, crumpled it and placed it under Jason's head. I turned his head to the side. My eyes sought out Amanda, the hyper-responsible over-achiever. "Go get Mrs. Linden. Now!" She was out the door without a backward glance.

Jason was into a full grand mal seizure, his entire body rigid and twitching, frothy saliva pouring from his mouth. I knelt next to him and looked up at the frightened faces. "Thank you all for helping. Now go stand quietly in the hallway." They filed out.

Dolly Linden arrived and went to Jason. "You all did the right things here." She paged the office. "Call an ambulance. We have a student in room 212 who's having an epileptic seizure."

Dolly stayed with Jason. I went to my students. They were abnormally quiet, concern etched in their young faces. "An ambulance is on its way. Jason will be fine. I'd like you to go sit in the library for the rest of the hour." Trevor refused to leave. He and I went back into the classroom and waited.

The ambulance arrived. The medics strapped Jason to a stretcher and carried him out. Dolly left to call Jason's mother.

Trevor picked up his saliva-drenched jacket and balled it up.

"Sorry about your jacket," I said.

"That's what washing machines are for." He stared at the floor where Jason had been. Then he went to the restroom and came back with handfuls of paper towel and soaked up the saliva. We put all the desks back in order. The bell rang.

"Thanks, Trevor."

He nodded and went to his second hour class.

🍎

Jason was absent on Tuesday. I gave the first speech of the day. I praised the class for keeping calm and thanked them for helping. "You will undoubtedly learn something about yourselves and each other from this experience." Teachers know that a shared significant emotional event bonds a class.

When he returned on Wednesday, Jason asked if he could change the topic for his speech. My brain ran through all the teacherly reasons why he shouldn't. My vocal chords didn't listen. "If you're sure you can have it prepared in two days, go for it."

🍎

Jason gave the last speech on Friday – an informative speech on epilepsy. Then he placed his note cards on the lectern and looked up at the class. He spoke of when he was diagnosed, of the various medications he had tried, how he found one that worked, how he hated taking it.

"In fact, I had stopped taking it. That's why I had the seizure. Guess I'll have to take it the rest of my life." He looked around at the class. "I figured you should know since you were here. I really want to thank all of you for helping me."

He looked down for a few seconds before saying, "Do you want to ask me anything?" Questions came, tentatively at first, and then poured forth.

Seated in the center row, last desk, I watched Jason speak with confidence and authority, that painfully shy boy only a shadow in his past.

CHAPTER FIVE

Sense and Nonsense

The mediocre teacher tells. The good
teacher explains. The superior teacher
demonstrates. The great teacher inspires.

—William Arthur Ward

JAMES HEIN

Tutoring with Richard

Dear Lisa,

Bet you didn't expect to hear from me so soon. But I figure we should be mature about this thing. I only wrote this letter to affirm your decision. You did the right thing. I thank you from the bottom of my heart for the week and a half we shared. And the two-hour honeymoon was especially beautiful. Don't worry about my jaw. The cast fits fine. I can't chew, but the supermarket has a sale on chicken soup and Jell-O this week. No big deal.

I'm thinking we shouldn't call each other. This will be my last letter.

> Best Wishes,
> Richard C. Tublewski

Dear Lisa,

Just want to drop you a quick note. And don't worry. I'm not fixating on you. I can let go. Anyway, I noticed just how roomy the apartment was now that you're gone. It's just great! No bed to clutter up the bedroom. No refrigerator or oven to take up all that space in the kitchen. We definitely did the right thing.

Call me or drop by anytime. But call first. I never know when I'm going to be in. I got a new job – I'm tutoring for the Fiction Writing Department at Columbia College Chicago now.

Best Wishes,

Richard

🍎

Dear Lisa,

I couldn't make the rent for the apartment this month. The pay for tutoring outright stinks. But don't worry about me. I'll live in the van.

I love my job though. Don't get me wrong. Tutoring at Columbia isn't strictly tutoring in the traditional sense, i.e., you take an ignorant fledging under your wing and allow them to have occasional glimpses into your infinite wisdom.

We mainly take the Read-to-Write Method of teaching writing from the classroom and apply it in a one-on-one setting in order to further enhance a student's reading, writing, recall and seeing-the-story-in-the-mind abilities. We read published material; retell it orally; comment on what we noticed; play some word games to get the imagination fired up; make up a telling; and then, of course, tell it orally; write it to the page; read it back – there's so much to it, I recommend an essay in *College English* titled "The Read-to-Write Method: Helping Students become Writers" by

Tamara Sobieski. It explains the whole process, and it's much more interesting to read than some old restraining order.

> Best Wishes to My One-Time Love,
> Richard

🍎

Dear Lisa,

I was sitting in the back of the van yesterday, staring at a picture of you and cleaning my gun, when I got to thinking about what you said to me on the phone last night. All I did was call you to let you know your mom's front porch light was burnt out, and you go and scream, "Leave me alone, Richie!" How am I supposed to take that? I would think, since I went out of my way to drive nine hours on a Tuesday night to check up on your mom, you'd be thankful.

Anyway, the new job's great. I meet with tutees inside a tiny little cubicle that has just enough room for the two of us to sit facing each other in tiny little chairs.

The main challenge of my job is to identify potential problems that tutees may have, bad habits or patterns, particular snags that may trip them up or hamper their development.

For instance, I have one tutee who imposes a "nannyish" voice onto a text when she reads aloud; she reads nearly everything like a baby-sitter reading a bedtime story. I realized, after a few sessions, that it was habitual, and I wondered how I would get her to stop.

At first, I wondered if the nanny voice was, indeed, her true voice, the voice she used in her everyday speech. Just talking with her showed that that wasn't the case. Now, I know that writings in a journal or diary are always a great tool for getting to a writer's voice. So we read a few of her journal entries, and, as I suspected, her true voice was much more real and sincere.

All I could do to help her drop the nanny was listen closely and coach as best I could. The first few sessions, I assigned readings where the voice was really strong. Especially so. Stuff like *Huck Finn, Moby Dick, Naked Lunch* – pieces where it would be harder than usual to impose an outside, unnatural voice. And, with these selections, I used the coaching methods recommended in Ms. Sobieski's essay I mentioned in my other letter. "Have students write a letter to a friend and put their essays in the letter. This will remind them that readers are real people," (Sobieski: 343-346).

Once, I even told her flat out, "Drop the nanny!"

She grinned slightly, looked at me and said, "Sorry."

Yep. That's right. She said she was sorry. It made me start to think. Some people apologize for nothing at all. While others who should apologize for ripping out hearts and acting like complete bitches never think to do so. These thoughts upset me so much, I think I overreacted a bit.

I leapt from my chair, stood over her and screamed, "No need to apologize for anything! I know it's hard to understand, but my coaching is *just that!* Not corrections or criticisms! Got it?! It's not *your* fault. Nothing's ever *your* fault! Now quit being so dumb and read!"

The tiny little thing jumped in her chair and stared at me from behind her thick-lensed glasses. The book slipped from her hands. She looked ready to cry until there was a knock at the door and a voice.

"Hello? Everything okay in there?"

She shouted out a hoarse, "No!"

Eventually, the office staff took me out to Michigan Avenue, roughed me up a bit and made me promise to cut my horseshit. *This is a college, not a boot camp!* After I told them I was really, really sorry, they let me back in. And her. She was shaken up. So they had the police take her home. That calmed her down.

Oh, well. I've bored you with enough details. Bored you enough about my life which I'm sure doesn't interest you. I promise I won't write you anymore.

Warmest Wishes, My One-Time Love,

Rich

P.S.: Last Saturday night at around two in the morning, I noticed a red and black Mazda pull up in front of your place and drop you off. Who was that guy? Have I met him? Just curious. Is his name Lorenzo? That's what was on his plate.

🍎

Dear Lisa,

This Saturday is our 4-month anniversary. The semester is over. My tutees are off for the summer, and I have nothing to do really. Want to go to lunch? Let me know soon. I'm waiting in your backyard.

Love Forever,

Richie

P.S.: Be careful when you walk out your house at night. The neighborhood is filled with loonies. That's why I have my gun.

MARILYN BATES

Empty Gesture

I spotted him right away – the black tee shirt, the belt with the chain, head shaved, one or two dreadlocks in the back. I never suspected that he might signal the end of my career as a creative writing instructor in a prestigious school.

I thought I was invincible then, charming all the students with my ability to get them to write. They were thrilled at what they were capable of producing, and some of the time they were thankful for being led into those productions. But he was a sniper's bullet, and our high school, a stock and barrel cocked at any teacher whose curriculum was, well, "edgy." And I was a little too immune to my own vulnerability.

At first, he didn't seem to have any friends in the class and sat by himself, propping one boot heel on the chair in front of him. I had had his kind before, the kind that scowled, tried to be intimidating the first day, tried to tell me he was trouble and not to mess with him. It didn't bother me a bit.

His name was Jason. When I started talking about the art of storytelling, he took a penknife out of his pocket and cleaned his fingernails. The penknife was contraband as far as the school was concerned, but I wasn't going to hassle him right off the bat. Probably he would run to see his counselor and drop the course after the first session, especially when I handed out the syllabus with the long list of papers and due dates. When the bell rang and the class emptied, he stopped at my desk.

"Can we write about anything?" he asked.

"Within the limits of propriety," I said.

"What's propriety?"

"You know – that little voice inside that says, 'I wouldn't read this in front of the pope.'"

"Good," he said, then folded the syllabus into his back pocket, strode out the room with his legs spread slightly apart as if straddling a horse.

When he handed in his first story, I was startled by the tale of a boy with a cruel father who lived in the wilderness with his mother and a big husky named Blaze. The boy's mother was unable to protect him from the father's drive to make him into a replica of himself. The story made me wonder about Jason's home life – if it was terrible, if it was the reason he shaved his head and strutted around with bare arms bulging out of a mangled tee shirt, looking so tough.

When class warmed up and they were into sharing stories, I read part of one that I was working on, modeling trust and mutual respect for ourselves as a community of writers. I had had complete freedom in developing the creative writing curriculum. Since I was a published author, class was conducted like a writing workshop as opposed to a standard English classroom. Although there were academic objectives involving the development of critical writing skills and producing grammatically correct work, content was my baby, and I used many well-respected journals such as *Nimrod* and *Ploughshares* as models.

Jason stopped at my desk after class and asked if he could read the end of my story. "Well, it's far from finished," I said. "And several pages long," I added, doubting his desire to read it all.

"I'd like to," he insisted. He took the manuscript with him. On Monday he came back with it, plunked it on my desk. "It's a good story."

"Oh?"

"Yeah, I like the way the woman gets away from the guy at the car wash, holding him off with the jet spray. Cool," he added.

Jason's stories grew weirder and weirder. One was about a character named Fejal, who survived in the wilderness, aping the actions of a wolf, ending up trapping and eating a rat. I knew it was designed to get everyone's attention, but the story was ingeniously written, the character believable, each step toward the climax perfectly timed. I believed that creative expression was a desirable entity, and I hated to cut a writer off at the knees by imposing content restrictions. I was worried, though, that his stories would skirt on the edge of what was an appropriate contribution to a high school class.

In a strange, unspoken way I was in competition with a newly hired young woman who once worked for the Associated Press but had no teaching experience. She wore a tan gabardine mackintosh belted around a slim figure and a quirky hat out of the 40's that reminded me of the serial radio reporter, Stella Dallas. And she made no bones about being thought of as an oddball for wearing it. Although I admired her pluck, I thought, there's a big difference between knowing how to write and knowing how to teach teenagers to write. Wait till she gets a load of how hard it is to manage students' personalities – to motivate! Still, I felt her presence in the background. Mine was a very popular class, with three sections bursting at the seams. It wouldn't take too much for her to be given one and then snap up the others if the least bit of controversy arose. A fine line existed between stimulation and stretching the limits of decorum. So what to do? How to encourage Jason's obvious talent yet justify the contents of his story in terms of standards required in typical English classes?

Once I was reprimanded by a stiff-necked department supervisor for using Tobias Wolfe's wonderful short story that appeared in the *New Yorker,* "A Bullet in the Brain," an ingenious account of a man standing in line at the bank who attempts to joke with the bank robber and is shot, hence the title. Particularly masterful is the technique of a long reverie that goes through the dying man's mind before he passes on, a wonderful amalgamation of his memories, in which a brief mention of his penis is innocently embedded in the tale. Nevertheless, I decided to give Jason's story of Fejal an A because he had created a totally believable, though repugnant, character.

At once his behavior changed. He seemed more animated during class, listening carefully to others and commenting on group members' works. Maybe it was a good thing to encourage him. The drafts were read in workshop fashion – in small groups before handing in the story. I ignored Jason's hand when it was time to share, hoping to read his privately at the end of the period in order to discover its contents.

Nancy cried out, "Mrs. Bates, you've got to hear Jason's story." Undaunted by my choosing another student to read, Jason passed his paper back to someone in the row who, after perusing a small part, blurted out, "This is a scream. Come on, Mrs. Bates, you have to let him read this."

I gave in but winced as he recited with delight a story entitled "Stir Fry," about two characters – a mortuary technician named Dr. Bletcher and his obsessive apprentice, Forbes. Dr. Blethcer pleasures in dissecting unclaimed corpses from the state mental institution and Forbes performs the grizzly chore of collecting the bodies and bringing them to Bletcher's mortuary. Forbes is also a Viet Nam vet who once enjoyed the pleasure of wiring enemy soldiers and detonating them:

Back in Nam, Forbes was a demolition man. When they were bored or stoned, he and his buddies liked to take gook POWs and attach them to explosives. He loved to watch those Oriental faces contorted in fear right before they shot into the sky, exploding into a shower of blackened Charlie.

The story ends when Forbes decides to rid himself of Bletcher in an uncanny and grizzly plot to electrocute his boss:

Later, Forbes returned with some hardware and a little something of his own creation. Bletcher called him into the mortuary, congratulating him on the retrieval of the bodies. The doctor felt a mild electric shock. Try as he might, he couldn't detach himself from his instrument. The shock increased as his arm fluctuated wildly. His legs seemed to act on their own, springing against the floor as though he were stamping out a fire. He began to take in deep breaths, grasping his chest with his free hand, fingers stiff as tines of a fork. Slowly, his limbs grew flaccid, and his lungs gave way. His eyes were ablaze with fear at his last look at Forbes, and his vision clouded over and closed."

I tried to cover my own distaste to the class by saying, "Well, let's look at the criteria on the assignment sheet and see if Jason's met them."

"Oh, come on, Mrs. Bates, you know this is an A paper," someone shouted from the back.

"Each assignment has an objective," I insisted, "and you have to meet the criteria." Now I was sounding like a sticky wicket.

My Chinese student, Nan, objected, "I think it's disgusting."

"Well," I countered, "he's certainly got our attention."

"He's just prejudiced," she insisted.

"Let's try the story without the racial overtones."

"No, no," someone objected. "It ruins the whole thing, the whole Nam motive, the title, 'Stir Fry.'"

Nan ran from the classroom, her face buried in long black hair. I knew there was going to be trouble, and before I could catch up with her, she vanished into the counselor's office down the hall. During the next period, I waited for the call from her counselor, Mrs. Williams. But that call never came. Instead the principal's secretary called, announcing that Mr. Raff would like to talk to me at the end of the day.

The entire meeting was a session of *j'accuse*. I bristled at the very idea that I "created a hostile atmosphere where the airing of prejudices can take place, encouraging the free venting of racial and gender bias." I left the office with a caveat: I was not to reward this kind of story, and I was to ask the student to turn in something "more appropriate." I was infuriated, but the real problem was how to face both Jason and Nan.

After class the next day, I did the cowardly deed and told Jason that someone had read the paper and objected to its content.

"I know who," he said, "just because it isn't politically correct."

"Well, you can see how it leaves itself open to that interpretation."

"It's not my feeling; it's the character's, for god's sake."

"Tell you what. I've got an idea. How about submitting it for publication elsewhere?"

"Whadda'ya mean *elsewhere?*" he asked.

"I know of a couple of journals that might like your story, and wouldn't it be better to be published outside of high school? Come on," I goaded.

"Like where?"

"Someplace like *Penny Dreadful* out of Hell's Kitchen, New York. I'm just betting they might like your story." The best I was hoping for was an encouraging note from the editor.

"Yeah, why not?"

"But you still have to hand in something to replace this assignment," I said.

"Nah, just give me a zero," he said.

"Jason, it's a big assignment, worth fifty points. Do you know what fifty points would do to your average?"

"I don't care," he said. "It's the principle of the thing."

So I averaged in the loss and fudged on the nine-week's grade. Luckily, he had a bounty of A's on assignments.

Nan was resolute. "I hate his kind," she said, "white, militia types who detest anyone of color."

She left me the perfect in. "Did it ever occur to you that you're stereotyping *him?*"

"What do you mean?"

"Well, it's a little bit like the characters in 'Sudden Storm,' a wonderful story we read in a recent edition of *The Atlantic Monthly.*" Then I digressed about the characters' perceptions of each other, trying with all my might to appease Nan. To be honest, I felt a little compromised in doing so. I prided myself on being honest with my students, and I felt that I was forced into taking the slick way out, that my answer was just a semantic argument, an empty gesture that wouldn't ring true in Nan's eyes. Somehow, she seemed appeased. Perhaps all she needed was some support for her contentions. I had given her that.

In six weeks *Penny Dreadful* had taken Jason's story. The editor signed the letter of acceptance with a pentagon. "Oh God," I thought. "What have I gotten myself into?"

Soon after, Jason flouted the red-covered journal. "Be careful where you spread this information," I said. "I know you're happy, and I am too. It shows how much talent you have. But the publication... you know who will say what." He could not contain his joy, however, and the news of it was broadcast everywhere. Colleagues asked me about it, said it was admirable to hold publication as a standard in my class. Fortunately, they were too busy to actually read the story, and there were no repercussions. At least not immediately.

Jason's story for the final assignment, one in which the main character, Aaron, was developed through dialogue, was a booby-trap. Called "Civil War," it was a debate between the body and the soul, but the body was the character's penis and the soul was his psyche. The ingenious part was that Jason never referred directly to the other speaker in the dialogue as Aaron's penis. He merely described the bathroom setting and just as Aaron unzipped his pants, "A voice came from below." Trapped in the bathroom, Aaron argues with his other side, justifying his abstinence as a sin, while his body tempts him with phrases like, "There's no denying it. It's a part of life, part of you. Anyway, sinning is a state of mind." The story ends with Aaron's psyche winning, but not until all the usual arguments have been exhausted.

Clearly, I was caught in a dilemma. The paper met all of the assignment's criteria and was a highly creative idea for a dialogue, transcending the usual high school conversations – the big party at someone's house, drug busts, traffic accidents or mafia killings. Still, I knew if I gave it the A it deserved, Jason would parade his story around the school, and I would be on the chopping block again for sanctioning it. Then I got a brilliant idea. I told Jason his was an excellent paper, but that I could not accept it because of the subject matter. I suggested he send it to Rider College's Creative Writing Contest for high school students and submit another story for the class assignment. He was psyched, and willingly handed in a less daring dialog, mailing his first story off to Rider.

In six weeks, the news came – Jason won a third prize in the fiction contest, the college willing to send a representative to present his $100 savings bond. The school newspaper ran an article about his award and asked for permission to print his prize-winning story in the next edition. I knew that once the editor and their sponsor read it, they would not run it. I tried to convince Jason that the best way to skirt the issue would be to write a clever synopsis, leaving out the salient details, but he was determined to flaunt it in their faces, every ounce of his rebellious nature announcing, "The world accepted my story, so there."

Shortly after, I was summoned to the office again. The proclamation was swift. A letter of reprimand would be placed in my employee file. Criteria for class stories and poems would be written by a committee selected by the English Department. I would teach one class of Creative Writing during the next year that would function as a trial. A standard writing textbook would be adopted, as opposed to excerpted stories from journals and magazines. Although it was a wonderful anthology, the proposed text focused on academic, as opposed to creative writing topics, such as Defining Rhetoric, Purpose and Thesis, Planning and Organization, etc. I was not to use *The New Yorker, Ploughshares,* or *Nimrod,* sources that modeled creative excellence, journals that students might one day aspire to.

The worst part was the letter of reprimand and the phrase: "encouraging deviant stories." This I took hard, not only because it was untrue but most of all, it was mean. I had been teaching this course for sixteen years, and many of my students had won writing awards – the National PTA Reflections contest, *Read* magazine's annual short story contest, the NEA , The Scholastic competition. One read his works at the Library of Congress in Washington. I felt discouraged and demeaned.

🍎

Interestingly enough, the very cause of my struggle drifted from my class at the end of the semester as easily as he entered. It felt strange not to receive a final goodbye from the one whose words I sought to protect at any cost. Or an acknowledgment of what others had lost on his account. Maybe that was all my job was meant to be – to give students my best, and know that I did, looking no further than that for any reward.

Still, the principal's censure had taken its toll. Forced to compromise my standards for creative writing, I knew the free enterprise of the imagination would be stifled among my students. It was time, I thought, to turn it all over to Stella Dallas.

VICKI SALLOUM

Miss Hotchkin, Racist

Omar Johnson sat quietly at the head of the conference-room table.

"As far as I'm concerned, Miss Hotchkin is a racist." He delivered the last word with low, implacable hatred. He stared defiantly at an invisible object at the center of the polished table and, after a momentary silence, looked boldly at the staring faces.

Dean Mark Rosenberg placed a fist on the surface of the table, tapped it with his knuckles. "That's a strong accusation, Omar."

The young man glared. "How else would you explain why the only two students in her class who got Ds are African-Americans – me and Shawntell Roberts?" He glanced imploringly at Rosenberg, who sat immediately to his left. "I missed one class the entire semester and got Bs on all my assignments, and she gave me a D for the course. I know two whites who didn't do hardly any assignments and missed at least three classes and ended up with Bs. I did some checking on Miss Hotchkin. I found out she had to go before another grievance committee last year. An African-American filed a complaint against her and that complaint was upheld. Isn't that right?" He turned to Dean Rosenberg.

Rosenberg sighed.

"And I'll tell you something else," he added. "Miss Hotchkin is incompetent. Everybody in the class laughed at her because she didn't know a damn thing about journalism."

Rosenberg turned to Miss Hotchkin. "Is there anything you'd like to say?" he asked.

Regina Hotchkin, two seats down from Rosenberg at the left side of the table, glanced around the room, inspecting the faces of the four faculty members and two students who comprised the committee. "What does one say," she asked, "when someone calls you a racist?" She turned to Omar. "You enrolled in my News Writing and Reporting class after taking another class from me the previous semester: Journalistic Interviewing. Why would you sign up for a second class if you thought I was a racist?"

"Because," he countered, "I didn't *know*." His eyes shifted from one to another, establishing contact, then moving on. "There were four of us in that interviewing class – me and three whites. At the end of the semester, she gave everybody As but me. My work was far superior to anybody else's. I'm an intern at the *Herald-Tribune* in the sports department. I had a 3.6 GPA till Miss Hotchkin messed it up. I'm gonna be a journalist when I graduate. My work was better, but I was the only one to get a B.

"When I came back from break, I called Miss Hotchkin. We met in the library. She showed me my final exam and pointed out what she called the 'problems,' so I thought maybe it was my fault. But," he said with growing enmity, "when I got this D in her news writing class, I knew something was really wrong. And what's wrong is she's a racist – besides being the dumbest instructor City College ever hired."

A spindly, silver-haired physics professor who had introduced himself as Eldridge Flanders coughed nervously and adjusted his glasses. "Miss Hotchkin," he asked, "why did you give him a D?"

"D+," she corrected. Miss Hotchkin's voice evoked the gentile quality of a Mississippi-bred woman, remarkably fragile, almost childlike, for someone in her fifties. It was a vocal instrument more suited to a campus library than a university classroom. Now it was particularly subdued, betraying a faint, quivering reticence. "He made a D+ because he made a 30 on his final exam." She lowered her head. "When I saw his paper," she continued, "I couldn't believe it. It was the worst effort of any student I've ever taught – and I've been a part-time instructor at four colleges and universities. And I want to tell you something else," she said with growing confidence. "This semester I also taught four classes at Mauritius Community College. Ninety-eight percent of my students there are black, and they *liked* me. They didn't think I was a –"

"Let's discuss the exam," Flanders interrupted. "What account-ed for his grade?"

She paused, then answered grudgingly. "It's not a pretty pic-ture. In one question, I provided notes taken from a published story about a traffic accident. I asked that they take these scram-bled notes and write their own story using a pyramid structure – in which the information is arranged from most important to least. Contained in these notes was information that a woman had died at the scene of the accident and a man had been criti-cally injured. Most people would know that fatalities and injuries belong in the lead. Omar didn't include that information any-where in his story. And the entire exam went like that, easy questions gone unanswered or simply answered incorrectly."

"Omar," said Dr. Flanders, "let's hear from you."

"Let me tell you about *her*," he shot back. "By the end of the semester, she'd so demoralized everybody with her ignorance and the stupid way she'd critique our stories without knowing what the hell she was talking about that we all wanted out. We wanted out of there. It was the worst class I've taken and other students have said the same. Dean Rosenberg talked to some of them. He can tell you."

A pale, freckle-faced woman tapped her pencil on the table. Her name was Nano O'Connor. She taught psychology and sociology.

"What about it, Mark?" she intoned.

Rosenberg shrugged. "Some expressed doubts about her expertise in the field. She said things that led them to believe she hadn't mastered the material."

"Such as?"

"She believes," Omar brightened, "that you can use featurish leads on breaking news stories."

"I did *not* say that!"

"She also said," he ignored her, "you can use anecdotal leads for hard news stories, and that's just plain ignorant. Students made fun of her. Once, when we were critiquing papers, they pretended to critique the stories the way she would, mimicking her tone of voice, repeating the stupid things she'd say. They were mocking her. She was a *joke*."

Her face turned crimson.

🍎

Amid the silence, her mind wandered to the night of Jason's story. Jason, a student in her class and friend of Omar, submitted a story about a student organization on campus that had elected new officers after four of the five previous officers had been forced to resign. Jason had buried the fact of the forced resignations near the bottom of the story, offering no explanations. Miss Hotchkin had pointed out that it was an important part of the story – readers had a right to know why the officers had been forced to resign. Jason laughed, saying that the organization's leadership did not wish that information revealed. He implied she had a tabloid reporter's taste for sensationalism.

"But it's not fair to the reader to withhold relevant information," she'd replied. "The fact that these officers were forced to resign is relevant. The reader has a right to know the reason why."

The students laughed – not harshly – but in a way that signaled their amusement at her earnestness. They laughed again when she critiqued Omar's stories. In one, he'd given statistics in such a careless manner that it completely misrepresented the facts. Jason quickly defended him. In another, vital facts were missing and assertions went unsubstantiated. It was a feature that cried out for the use of multiple sources, yet Omar had only interviewed one. Again, Jason defended him. She went home that night baffled by their inability to see glaring defects in the story.

With each class, she'd discover other defects in their stories. Yet, the more she pointed them out, the more vehemently they disputed her. With a faltering self-confidence, she began to pore over the text, practically memorizing chapters to reinforce the knowledge she had gained as a staff writer for three newspapers, though her journalism career had long been over.

On days she did not teach, she awakened early in the morning and worked late into the evening, studying chapters, creating lesson plans, grading and critiquing papers. She bought Sunday issues of the best newspapers in the country – *The Washington Post, The New York Times* – to clip out stories to show these students the very best reporting, very best writing and the different types of story structures she had introduced them to in class, structures not commonly used by reporters of the *Herald-Tribune,* a mediocre paper at best. It didn't work.

She thought personality differences would fade and the material would take over. The material was what counted. But with this class it didn't work. She'd be lecturing and look up and see Rita and Rhoda silently mouthing her words and making funny faces. Her concentration broken, she would notice herself stumbling over words or forgetting what she was about to say. Struggling to keep the momentum going, she would look up again, and they would be giggling. She would cling to her written notes, as if there was nothing inside herself to believe in anymore, and things would further deteriorate until, unable to finish the lesson, demoralized, defeated, she would let them out early.

Once, when she let them take a fifteen-minute break (the class lasted three hours), students drifted back into the room except for Jason, Rita, Rhoda and Omar. She and the remaining students waited another twenty minutes until finally a student volunteered to go get them. They had been sitting on the front steps of the building, gossiping. Their zany spirits infiltrated the lesson on crime reporting, with Rhoda laughing uproariously, making grossly inappropriate horse-like sounds in a manner so rude Miss Hotchkin thought the girl might be on drugs.

Then the mimicking began. She had saved the final forty minutes of class to evaluate students' stories. Jason volunteered to go first. With rapid-fire speed, he began to imitate the way Miss Hotchkin would critique a story, repeating her comments in an exaggerated tone of voice – comments that had no relevance to the student's work before him, but uttered for the sole purpose of making fun of their teacher – and Rita and Rhoda, catching on, continuing with the fast-paced, irreverent critiquing, not missing a beat nor paying one iota of attention to the merits of the student's work, until Miss Hotchkin, a look of devastation suffused across her face, waited for the proper moment then said: "You may go home."

Perhaps it was the manner in which she said it or the look of anguish upon her face that attributed to the stunned silence. No one moved. They continued to stare and she at them, a fiery hatred in her eyes now. Almost in unison, students nervously jammed books into satchels and rushed out of the room. She heard the muffled voices of two students who had remained, then the footsteps of one leaving.

She heard the voice of Julia Moore, an older student, gently trying to get her attention. "Miss Hotchkin," she said kindly. "We're not all like them." She paused. "Some of us are very serious about journalism. We want to learn. They're just immature. You let us know in the beginning what the rules were. I've never seen anything like this in any other class."

Miss Hotchkin walked home that night in shock. She put on

her nightgown and knelt to caress her kitten. Somehow she lost her balance and collapsed on him, sending him yelping under the bed. She turned to look at herself in the full-length closet mirror and saw reflected in her eyes a grotesque agony.

The next morning, she went to see her boss, a slim, erudite young man from Pakistan who was the media arts director. She told him she did not wish to teach again the next semester or any semester; she did not think she was a good teacher; things simply were not working out. He had been compassionate, said he genuinely regretted she wouldn't be back. Only a few more classes remained. She over-prepared as usual so that she could recite exact pages from the text in case any of her students disputed her.

Then exam night arrived. One glance at Omar's exam booklet after he'd turned it in and left the room told her without a doubt more trouble lay ahead.

🍎

"What Omar said is true," she said to the gathering at the table. Dean Rosenberg sat impassively drawing cartoon figures on a legal pad. "Some of these students did mock me. I would go home at night after these incidents thinking maybe they were right. After all, they were so *confident.*

"But you know what, Dean Rosenberg?" She looked anxiously at him. "At night when I read some of the stories they submitted, I saw these problems. I saw important information that belonged in the lead buried in the body of the story. I saw information in the lead that was not explained in the rest of the story. I saw opinions that went unsubstantiated. Or material that barely had any relationship to the lead, structures completely disorganized, stories rambling and confused. I saw vital facts left out or stories with no attribution or that blatantly libeled people, and I knew I had something to teach them. And I went back to class feeling good about myself because I knew I had something to offer, that not only did they not know how to write, they didn't know how to interview.

"Many of my students don't want to be print journalists. They want to be broadcast journalists – and it has nothing to do with carrying the message. It has to do with the glamour and the money – the prestige it will bring them. It's all so... *superficial.*"

They looked blankly at her, and then Omar, half rising, looking as if he wanted to kill her, said, "I want to be a print journalist." His fury turned to desperation, and, as she gazed into his frantic eyes, she suddenly felt sorry for him, a shame washing over her. Things had turned out so badly. She couldn't understand it or explain it. "I'm a good reporter," he pleaded, "and you're goddamn trying to destroy me – !"

"Omar – "

"Miss Hotchkin!"

Half-standing, half lunging, staring bitterly at Miss Hotchkin, Omar reluctantly sat down when Rosenberg lay a hand on his shoulder. "That's quite enough!" Rosenberg turned to Miss Hotchkin. "Let's take a look at his papers."

He passed around copies of Omar's five graded stories and the group silently perused them, noting the grade for each assignment and Miss Hotchkin's critiques. Dr. O'Connor spoke first.

"I see he made four Bs and one B+. If he's such a bad journalist, why did you give him Bs?"

"I didn't say he was a bad journalist. He has the potential to make As. But the fact is, much of his work is C work. I gave him Bs hoping that would encourage him to take more time with his assignments."

"More time?" Omar exclaimed. "Do you know what I do with my time? My mama can't afford to pay for my schooling so I work two jobs – I'm a waiter at night and an intern in the day."

"I also happen to know he does volunteer work with AIDS babies," Dr. O'Connor said. "I'm an AIDS counselor at Charity Hospital, and I see him there." She placed an elbow on the table, resting her chin in her hand. She stared at Miss Hotchkin. "Maybe you're expecting too much. These City College students have jobs. They're not rich like the day students. Many are disadvantaged kids who are working their tails off."

"I'm concerned," Dr. Flanders added, "that so many students seem to think you're a bad teacher. They can't all be wrong, can they?"

She searched for an explanation. Something that would explain it. She obviously didn't inspire confidence. She was not by any stretch of the imagination an intellectual. She did not have a strong ego, and she knew that it showed. It had been fifteen years since she'd been a practicing journalist; that sounds like an eon to students. In her reporting days, she'd worked herself up to a staff position on one of the country's most respected papers; it wasn't by accident. She'd gotten there by pure will, almost superhuman effort. She'd worked so hard that she'd finally burnt herself out.

But fifteen years out of the profession puts doubts in people's minds and this, coupled with her voice and diffident ways and the fact she was a print, not a broadcast, journalist, which was what most of her students wanted to be, accounted for much of the problem. And she wasn't a dazzling lecturer. She was a reporter more than a teacher; she knew that now. And she rued her decision years ago to leave the profession.

But one thing she did know: she *knew* her journalism. And it nearly killed her when Omar or Jason disputed what she said, absolutely convinced they knew better than she things her editors had drilled into her consciousness over the course of a dozen years, things she'd learned by pure repetition and agonizing hard work and drudgery – good reporting comes from that – and, most recently as a teacher, by poring over the texts to reinforce what she knew from experience and by scrutinizing the best stories in the land. Still they wouldn't believe her, these students who never studied, never had a thing published in their lives. There were nights she felt like a child who'd found a dead body on the beach, and nobody will believe her and nobody will come to see.

On nights when they discounted her, she would go to her classes the next morning soul-sick from humiliation. And there, at Mauritius, she would see luminous on their faces the love these students had for her and absolute belief. There, she taught remedial English to beginning students, some of whom couldn't even put a sentence together. Their essays were like dense jungle thickets, barely decipherable word choices, tortured grammar, no punctuation, a tangled, impenetrable forest leading nowhere. She'd taken the most wanting – Kyshatiara Amise, Tamekia Foder, Dai Duc Trune – and tutored them in the library in her free time, working for hours with each separately until an understanding shone in their eyes, until they finally for the first time in their lives began to write in clear, direct and simple sentences.

She began to mend with each act of kindness. When they handed in their final projects – the journals she'd asked that they keep – she saw written on the last page of one: "Miss Hotchkin, you are my mentor." Another: "You are a wonderful teacher. I will always remember you." A student came to her desk and said: "I've been in the remedial classes three times. You're the only one that bothered to teach us." At the end of the semester, more students in her classes passed the Exit Exam – graded, not by her, but by the other teachers in the department – than those in all the other classes. The Exit gauged minimum competency. If a student failed, he went on to the next level of remediation; if he passed, he went straight to English 101. Teachers came up to her in the halls and asked how she ever got her students to write such well-developed essays. She should give a seminar, they told her, on how to pass the Exit.

🍎

"I don't know how to answer that," she said weakly to Dr. Flanders. She gazed at a stain on the thin gray carpet. "I'm only one person. I haven't put all the pieces of the puzzle together."

Dean Rosenberg spoke: "Let's pass around Omar's exam."

They examined each of ten questions and Omar's responses.

"What's wrong with his answer to this fifth question?" asked Dorathea Coulter, a student representative to the committee. "You took off 15 points."

Miss Hotchkin looked at it. In Question 5, she'd provided

three newspaper stories and asked that they identify the type of structure for each.

"Omar misidentified each type of structure," she replied.

Dr. Flanders, eyeing the exam, said in a casual, neutral voice: "I see here you let them know where you found each story. You got them from *The Washington Post, The New York Times,* and *The Wall Street Journal,* is that right?"

Miss Hotchkin nodded. "I found stories that were examples of certain types of structures."

"But that's just your opinion." Flanders looked up. "Surely it's subjective as to what kind of structure they are."

"No," she said adamantly. "The stories I selected are clear examples of the hourglass, the *Wall Street Journal* formula, and the list technique. Omar misidentified every – "

" – But surely that's opinion. This is not exact science."

"Dr. Flanders," Miss Hotchkin retorted. "Sir...do you know *anything*...about journalism?"

He lowered his chin, stared disdainfully over his glasses. "No, I have never formally studied it, but I do have common sense."

"Miss Hotchkin," Dean Rosenberg interjected. He kept his gaze away from her. "Omar has been a good student. He has a 3.6 GPA. A D in this class would mean he would lose his scholarship. Since he's made Bs on all his assignments, why don't we just give him a B for the course?"

"Dean Rosenberg," she pleaded, "those five stories you passed around are not all the stories I assigned. He failed to hand in the last three. I excused him from two because he said his mother had been sick, and he'd flown to Arizona to see her. But there's no excuse for not doing the last assignment or for making a 30 on his final exam, which represented thirty percent of the final grade."

"I, too, think you should give him a B," Dr. O'Connor concurred. "He only missed one class, he's gotten Bs on the work he did turn in – "

"And if I change his grade, do I change Shawntell Roberts', too? And if I do that, isn't that unfair to the students who earned their Bs?"

She struggled to contain herself. "You see… I had some students who *did* work hard. Diana Harrington took off from work an entire week to study for exams. Julia Moore stayed long after the others had gone – she stayed the entire four hours because she cared about her grade. Omar was practically the first to leave. He barely stayed an hour."

"Is that why you gave him a 30 – vengeance?" asked Dorathea.

"Vengeance?" said Miss Hotchkin. "How about laziness?" She saw O'Connor's eyes flash with anger. "Omar didn't even bother to answer the last two questions. They were about libel – isn't that important?"

"Certainly," Dean Rosenberg said irritably, "but I think you've been too harsh."

"But… he made a 30. He didn't even do his last *assignment!*"

"You know what that last assignment was?" Omar scowled. "She asked us to interview a public official about an issue that affects the city. No public official is gonna waste time being interviewed by a student!"

"I've given that assignment to every class I've taught," she said heatedly. "Some students came back with interviews with non-officials – because the assignment was too hard for them. But the majority of them triumphed. There was victory on their faces because it was so hard and they got it done.

"What do you think reporting is?" She glanced frantically around the room. "It's being repeatedly rebuffed but continuing to try because you have to. It's doing difficult assignments and working your butt off to get the story because that's what you've been hired to do. What the hell am I training them for – I'm training them to be *journalists*."

"You won't give me a B? Is it because I'm African-American?"

Miss Hotchkin sat stunned, a look of astonishment on her face. She groped for words, found none, bent her head and closed her eyes. "It used to be black was beautiful," she said quietly, tears in her eyes. She looked up, smiling. "Is that out of fashion, too?"

A gasp filled the silence.

"I think Omar's question is good." There was an edge to Flanders' voice. "Does race have anything to do with this?"

"Now we get to the question."

She seemed visibly to relax, as if there was absolutely no reason to be accountable anymore. "This city has the highest murder rate in the country," she said in a tone just above a whisper. "And most of the violence is committed by blacks. That's no surprise – look at the statistics. And do you know who I blame? It isn't poverty. It's the mothers. They're breeding animals in the streets. Nobody has bothered to teach these children *decency*."

Her voice was barely audible: "Two days ago, another beautiful girl was raped and murdered in this city. I haven't been able to get it out of my mind." She looked up. "And why is it I'm not surprised the murderer was black?"

Shocked murmurings penetrated the silence, but she didn't care. She was now almost enjoying it. "You want to know if I'm a racist? Let's not talk about criminals, let's talk about students. I've taught blacks in four schools. It's almost as if there are two kinds: those who think they have every right to everything simply because they're black, and those who work their heads off. They never complain, never give up, they work twice as hard as everybody else." Miss Hotchkin stood up. "It's not because he's black I gave him a D. But maybe the reverse can be said of you. If this student were white and affluent – and put forth this little effort – we wouldn't be sitting here now. It's exactly because he's black and, as you say, 'disadvantaged' that we're going through all of this.

"It can be said this student 'works his tail off,' as you so delicately put it, Dr. O'Connor, but he doesn't work his tail off in my class. His work is mediocre, lazy, sloppy. But then again, none of you gives a damn about journalism. None of you gives a damn about truth. You don't know what it's like to work till exhaustion. You're not seekers. You're not questioners. You're half-assed academics. You're politically correct, mediocrity-seeking parasites."

With that, she left the room.

🍎

In the end, they ruled against her and gave Omar his B. In a letter signed by every committee member and mailed to her two days later, they said they were "dumbfounded" by her "stereotypical" attitude and that she shouldn't be teaching. They suggested she take a "sensitivity" course then find another profession. They branded her with the "R" word, but what did it matter? She didn't care.

It was over. She would never teach again. And in the final analysis, this committee had gotten one thing right: she didn't belong in this profession. She was not a good teacher. When you're good, and this she had come to realize in the anguished days following the hearing, your students get better in their work, not worse, as was the case with Omar. Your students usually like you, even if you're tough as nails, but there was a bitterness and animosity that infected her class that was debilitating and unhealthy. She did not know exactly what she'd done to cause it, but suspected she'd been too harsh in critiquing their work, discouraging them rather than giving them the courage to go on. She did not really care about the students – the material was everything. For a real teacher, the student was everything.

CAROLYN HOWARD-JOHNSON

Remembering Winter

Winters in Utah can be bitter. The February wind moved the raindrops across my windshield like moiré but nothing else stirred. There was not a leaf or a blade of grass left for the polar blast to bend to its will. I veered off Highway 15 on a whim and had only a California-weight sweater as defense against the wind's bite. Everything heavier was packed away in the trunk. Still, when the rain slowed to a light drizzle, I pulled myself from the car as if called to a mission, hunched the sweater around my neck and ears with my shoulders and stared.

The school was a monolith named Ulysses S. Grant. The two stories of cubed granite blocks appeared large now only because of its isolation. It was a flat, gray school-and-mountain stage prop. Harsh and dull, the mountain was a theatrical backdrop with improper lighting. The sky was the color of the bottom of a stainless steel frying pan and looked just as flat.

The shirred wind sharpened my reaction, left my eyes bare to forgotten memories. I thought it would be interesting to revisit the place, kind of fun to see if the pictures in my mind – all soft and sweet and fuzzed by time – matched reality.

🍎

The children in the schoolyard looked like children from a remote decade. No color. A black and white film. The wind blew their voices away from me. No sound. Slow motion.

There was a child in the central portion of my brain who was new at school. New in town. She had come from a different place, a different background, and a different religion. She did not fit into the frame but there she was. She, unlike the others, was wearing colors, a blue snowsuit, a red hat and red mittens. She was the only child puffing dragon-like into the school door in leggings, fat and baggy around her legs, leggings that must be pulled, off and on, depending on the activity, indoors or out.

The other little girls wore wonderful long stockings shored up by the gadgetry of metal clips and belts hanging around their waists. Stockings with no elasticized thread. Stockings of ribbed dirty beige that tried to duplicate a neutral skin tone. They hung away from the knees and clumped at the ankles like folds of skin on puppies. It was difficult to understand how the little girl in the red hat could have coveted those long stockings, but she did.

"Eat big breakfasts for energy in the wintertime," the teacher had drawled in a deep, disinterested voice. "All students should wear undershirts, and boys should wear long underwear." A pause. "Girls should wear long stockings to protect their legs from winter draughts." There was only one little girl in Mary Janes and white anklets in the room. Always the last out to recess because of the leggings she must put on, Nina sat on the floor of the coatroom and tried to avoid the puddles of melted snow that slicked the linoleum squares.

The teacher was Nina's first male teacher. Her mother and the lady who lived next door wondered aloud, calling back and forward, as they pinned sheets and towels and underpants to the clothes lines, just why he was teaching in such a small town, why he didn't work for his father's construction company. Nina didn't care. She only wanted him to like her as her other teachers had. She wanted to bring his voice out of monotone, his colors out of drab, his face into focus.

The memory hovered there. Oval facelessness. My brain felt like a montage of quick, reeling pictures. Picture. Stop. New Scene. Stop.

Nina sat with her white ankle socks carefully rolled down once, galosh stains around the lower part of her calf. In sterile rows, the desk sat attached with nowhere else to go. Their legs were carved into cast iron curlicues, the tops scarred with geometrics engraved by small specters of the past. Nina fidgeted. She had finished her work early. She passed notes. She giggled with row mates. She nudged another.

The teacher scratched his chalk across the board. "All right! Class! I have warned you for the last time. There will be no recess today. All of you will suffer for the few who misbehave. You may go to the boys' and girls' rooms, one at a time, and return to your desks where you will sit, hands folded, until recess time is up."

Well, as least Nina wouldn't have to put her leggings on. Nina watched children shuffle silently, one by one, down the aisles to the bathroom. It became difficult to sit, almost painful to sit without moving. Or without talking. Nina was the reason there was no ringing of recess bells. Nina was the one who caused everyone to sit morosely in the blackboard and gray room. If she told him she knew she was the guilty one, he would let the others go and keep her. They could play. She wouldn't have to put her leggings on.

Perhaps he would like her better whether she wore long stockings or not.

Nina could see her shiny shoes stepping up the dark oil planks of the schoolroom floor. Parked under the man's desk were his feet in shiny shoes and little half-rubbers that he hadn't taken off. My adult brain remembered the name of the teacher. "Mr. Johnson, I want to talk to you about losing recess..." She looked up into the dull oval of memory's face. "I don't think it's fair. I want to..." *Apologize* would have been the next word. I remembered it as if it was on my lips at that very moment. The word stayed there, never uttered, at the back of the child's throat. It felt as if it was still there, cold and hard down around my voice box.

Mr. Johnson stood, pushing his chair back with a force that tumbled it backwards, into the blackboard with a cracking noise, like lightning in the silenced room. The faces of the students, small and white, looked toward us, eyes bright and frightened. The electric noise zip-zagged a crack up the blackboard.

"Nina here doesn't like being kept in for recess," this teacher said in a voice sarcastic but carefully controlled, frighteningly composed. The child in my memory stood without feeling her body, unable to interrupt, to explain. There was a furor about to spill around her.

"Nina," the teacher snarled, "doesn't think." The teacher put his hand on her head as if it were a stick shift, controlling, guiding her head around to face the class. "It's fair..." He slammed his fist on the desk and waited a long, silent time. "that no one got recess today." The child at his side didn't dare look at him. She didn't dare see the class. Her eyes filled with tears, and I could feel them as I stood in the frosted wind, traveling warm rivulets down bitter cold cheeks.

"Nina, of course, is the reason you are all kept in. Nina doesn't know how to behave," he said. "Nina doesn't know how to fit in. I suggest you all tell Nina how angry you are with her for making you lose your recess," the teacher said.

The child heard "fit in," "fit in" with the throbbing of her heart.

"Know how to fit in" with the shuffle of her shoes back to her desk.

"Know how to fit in " trying to will the tears to absorb back into her head so they wouldn't shame her more.

"Know how to fit in" as she pulled on her leggings and her galoshes.

"Know how to fit in" as her red boots slogged into brown mud on the rocked road home.

"Know how to fit in!" she yelled at the foothills, waiting for their echo back to her in the icy, brittle air.

And the mountains did echo, "fit in," "fit in." At first it was a childlike voice and then more like my own as I stood at the edge of the schoolyard.

❧

No one heard. Not the phantom children of the schoolyard, not the leafless trees or the old schoolhouse. I dropped my sweater from its huddled position around my body and felt the chilling effect of the wind creep under my clothing and ice my skin. I climbed into the car that had brought me this distance, silently, my ungloved hands sticking to the steering wheel, turned around and headed south. Winters in Utah can be bitter.

CHAPTER SIX

Teacher's Guide

Those having torches will pass them on to others.

—PLATO

RICHARD HAGUE

A Curmudgeon's Book of Lists: Take Two

In America, there's special stuff for every occasion and every job or hobby. There's decorating stuff for St. Patrick's Day and custom optical wear for sky divers and rock hounds, there's special lip balm for spelunkers and sew-on patches for bass fishermen, there's stuff for celebrating Groundhog Day and Cinco de Mayo and Juneteenth, and there's even some high-priced electronic stuff for that nice surveillance specialist on your list.

And there's stuff for teachers – I know, because I have a stack of catalogs about a foot high at the end of my desk, and sometimes I dip into it to see the latest in teaching tackle and gear. I see the complete works of Shakespeare on CD-ROM, I see software to calculate your grades on, book bags with the mugs of famous writers on them, coffee mugs with the names of famous writers on them, and little stick-on memos in as many neon colors as a sonnet has lines.

What I dislike about this teacher's stuff is that so often it is sickeningly cute. Even in high school classrooms, where we ought to

144 • RICHARD HAGUE

have arrived a slightly greater sophistication, students are sur-
rounded by posters featuring grotesquely adorable, huge-eyed
infants, so stunningly sentimental that even Mike Ditka would be
moved to weepy tenderness.

And there's this silly cuteness in other educational stuff, too.
For example, I have here before me a page from a teacher
publication specializing in building self-esteem and in creating
tolerance for diversity, two pretty good ideas.

But what has caught my eye is this one-page article, illustrated
by a cute little drawing of a man and woman, obviously onstage,
carrying cute little canes and wearing top hats and doing a cute
song-and-dance vaudeville routine. Teachers, I presume. Above
them the title reads: "100 Rules For A Successful And Happy
Life."

The thing about rules is that people who need them most are
the ones least likely to read something like this – or ever to read
anything, for that matter. That there are permanent absentees
from the middle-class Chautauqua doesn't seem to deter the
publishers of this stuff, though. They keep right on cranking it
out, following in the footsteps of good old Ben Franklin, who was
among the first Americans to publish a list of rules for the
improvement of life. The redeeming thing about Franklin was
that he was man enough to admit failing his own program.

So what does this most recent recipe for heaven on earth pre-
scribe? Number One: "Work hard." Now there's an original idea.
In case you didn't get Number One the first time around
(perhaps the writer thinks you're really stupid, but is afraid he
will wreck your self-esteem by saying it directly), Numbers Three
and Four say, "Put your nose to the grindstone," and "Put your

shoulder to the wheel." Sounds a lot like "work hard" to me. Maybe the real title of this should have been "27 Rules For A Successful and Happy Life – Some Repeated Three or Four Times In Slightly Different Ways Because We Think You're A Dunderhead."

The list goes on in the same vein. Number Twenty Three, for example, says, "Be happy for the success of others, even if they don't deserve it." So I imagine myself applauding the Robber Barons of the late 19th and early 20th centuries, whose exploitation of a generation of my Irish and Polish working-class ancestors in coal mines and steel mills made them millions in pre-income tax days. After all, according to this rule, I'm supposed to affirm their success, shooting them a thumbs-up and crying, "Right on, brothers!"

So when I get to Number 51: "Be smart," I see they can't really mean that, and that their rules are silly and shallow, criminally ignorant of the complexities of contemporary life.

In fact, I get so angry (thereby breaking Rule Number 86: "Lighten up") that I can't help it – I start writing my own set of rules, rules not for a "successful" life or a "happy" life, as defined by the cutesy-wootsey crowd, but for an Interesting Life, keeping in mind the old Chinese saying, "May you be born in interesting times." The saying, of course, is a curse.

Some Rules For An Interesting Life
1. Loaf a lot. Hang out, waste some time.
2. Screw a few things up and see what happens.
3. Become a fanatic in some bizarre field – know a lot about parasites, or St. Sebastian, or Iceland.

4. Adopt an abandoned lot in your neighborhood and take care of it as if it were a child. Your own.

5. Get righteously angry at least once a day.

6. Avoid buying new clothes more than once every four years, longer if at all possible.

7. Boycott amusement parks and suburbs.

8. Take the bus.

9. Argue with the people you respect the most.

10. Affirm the risky or downright crazy: "much madness is divinest sense."

And finally, number 11:

Grow up; invent your own rules.

MICHAEL O'ROURKE

High Plains Drifter

I avoided college teaching for several years. "I'll dig ditches before I teach freshman composition," was my refrain. I remembered my own freshman experience – the phony "themes" on subjects that didn't interest me (even if in other contexts they did interest me); the interminable tedium of the research paper requirement; the "boring" essay anthology – and knew I didn't want to be party to that. But then at the age of thirty, having done little with the latter half of my twenties but the equivalent of digging ditches (while play-acting at being a writer), I decided it was time to get serious about *something*. I returned to school, bought another advanced degree, and at thirty-three found myself smack in the middle of the high, flat, dry, wide-open, tree-less Texas panhandle, at what was then called West Texas State University, teaching (yep) composition.

I knew nothing.

I sometimes wonder what, if anything, those first couple of years of green, unwitting freshmen managed to learn from me about writing. What are their memories of freshman English?

Did they know how utterly powerless I felt, under my guise of self-assurance, to teach them anything? Did they know that I was just stumbling around, that each new, carefully-composed writing assignment was just an "essay," an attempt, a pedagogical shot into the dark of our collective ignorance? Am I, for some few of them, that one instructor who made a difference, or just the skinny guy with a big mustache who didn't bloody their own attempts, as they had expected – or not even that? How many of them, looking back, perceived the complete lack of plan, of progression, in the course, and saw instead what was the truth – that it was just a semester-long jumble of "Let's try this"?

I'd had no contact with freshman since I myself was a freshman, and hadn't read any freshman writing but my own. In '68 when I started college, "peer evaluation" and "workshopping" weren't in vogue (at least not where I went to school), so I had no idea what to expect. I did make two observations almost immediately: freshmen were masters of the empty generalization, the vapid cliché, the paper-that-talks-but-says-nothing, and they couldn't take the *parts* of a subject, and assemble them into a whole without some simple-minded "model," which I steadfastly refused to provide. In short, they had no instincts as writers, no sense of balance or pacing or shape, no feel for detail, which was "boring." Okay, they didn't read, but they did go to the movies, they did listen to music – why no sense of something "put together" from that? How did they manage, for example, to write about "raising cattle" or "growing cotton" or "buying a horse" (this was Texas, remember) and completely avoid discussion of the subject at hand? They were as clueless about writing as I was about teaching it, and their papers were as scatter-brained as my course.

Oddly enough, my own writing had begun to take off, now that it wasn't the sole focus of my attention. I'd been looking the other way for a couple of years, first at graduate school and then at this teacher dilemma, and now looked back...and could see quite clearly what I'd been struggling for years to find. I'd been a clenched fist as a writer, tight and anxious (like my students!), and found that if I just relaxed, just loosened my grip (still gripping, but loosely), and trusted myself, the words would come. Not in Thomas Wolfe torrents, mind you, but at least in a steady trickle, and having been dry as the landscape around me for several years, that was torrent enough.

How could I teach my students to relax? For perhaps that was it: loosen them up, divert their attention, induce them to look the other way. Yes, there was "free writing" and its various manifestations, but whenever we stopped those things and it was time to start writing "for real," they tightened up. How could I get them to loosen their grip? How could I teach them in a semester what it had taken me nearly a decade to learn for myself?

Write about what you know. But it didn't work – or, like everything else, it worked part of the time with *some* of my students, but not enough to make me feel I was "teaching" writing. So what if I had them write about what they *didn't* know?

🍎

The water tower in Canyon, Texas, was within walking distance of campus. One day, not knowing quite what I was doing or where it would lead, I said, "Leave your books in the room and come with me." We started walking ("Where are we going?" "Where are you taking us?" "What's going on?"), and when we reached the water tower, which was encircled by a chain-link fence in a sun-blasted vacant lot, I said, pointing up at it, "For next Wednesday, I want a thorough, accurate description of *that*. Typed. A minimum of one full page."

Huh?

Then I walked back to my office.

The descriptions, as I knew they'd be, were mediocre: neither thorough nor accurate, many shy of minimum length, and uniformly dull.

So for the next Wednesday, I handed out slips of paper on which were written the following assignment:

Canyon Water tower #2

1. *Describe the Canyon water tower in such a way as to suggest it is an eyesore.*
2. *Then describe it in such a way as to suggest it is a proud symbol of the community.*

Both descriptions must be "accurate": you can't make anything up. Also, your descriptions can't contain any explicit evaluations or generalizations, such as "The Canyon water tower is an eyesore" or "The Canyon water tower is a proud symbol of the community." Find ways to suggest its appealing or unappealing appearance with stating it. Show, don't tell.

Okaaay.

This time I took up their papers and read them aloud cold (anonymously and randomly). As I read, I pointed out language that was evaluative and abstract, and language that was specific and concrete. I noted descriptions that failed to communicate either "appealing" or "unappealing" or both, and identified places where "appealing" language had crept into an "unappealing" description and vice versa. But there were also some good descriptions and otherwise weak descriptions with good parts – concrete details, selective details, figurative language, associative connections – and when those came up, I said, "Yes. That's good writing. That line works."

Next I turned the water tower into "environmental art," a giant sculpture erected by the famous/infamous "Lorenzo Grandioso." The whole town is in an uproar. Letters – pro and con – are pouring in to the editor of the local paper. Write yours.

More random reading aloud, better and better writing – and one kid, the brightest student in the class, had Lorenzo write a letter.

Bingo.

The wilder the assignments got – the less my students "knew" about the subjects I had given them – the better the prose that flowed from them became.

...You're a hermit who lives in the water tower (the tank itself) in the ghost town of Canyon, Texas. Describe your life.

...Water towers have become obsolete, Canyon's is no longer in use, and the city is trying to decide what to do with it (besides tear it down). People are writing letters to the editor with their proposals. Write yours.

...The Cult of the WaterTower Worshippers has sprung up in Canyon, Texas. Cultists are flocking to the city from all over the country, and assembling at the base of the water tower to practice their religion. More controversy, more letters. Write yours.

...You're the mayor of Canyon, and the city has just narrowly escaped a major disaster, the poisoning of the water supply by Libyan terrorists. Three people dead, many still hospitalized. Huge controversy over whether city officials acted quickly enough. You give a speech on TV to the citizens of Canyon in an effort to calm them down, aware that you are up for re-election in two months. Write that speech.

I had tricked my students into loosening up by giving them assignments they perceived as so bizarre that loosening up was the only possible response. A few remained tight, a few refused to play my game, but the majority genuinely improved, and some of the transformations were remarkable. By the end of the term, almost all my students were more fluent, more flexible writers – more capable of adjusting to different rhetorical situations, to put it like the owner of a second advanced degree – than they had been at the beginning. They looked forward to those Wednesdays, to hearing what they had written, to receiving their next challenge, and I did too, not knowing if this week's "essay" would work, if it would prove too much of a challenge, too difficult or too "crazy" for my students to meet.

But I never know, at the outset, if any of my essays will work. And what I found out that semester was that even in the high, dry Texas plains I could draw from those green, unwitting freshmen what I wanted: water.

MARION STERN

Chicago Urban Skills Institute: a Valiant Effort, 1978

"I think we should have foreplay in this class." That's Florence trying to get a rise out of us before I can assign the new work. Her round eyes fix on Dorothy, her academic rival and the only other American-born student in the class.

"You mean free play," Dorothy has fallen for the bait.

Dorothy's t-shirt boldly and succinctly tells her story in red magic marker:

I am a virgin

This is a very old T-shirt

Dorothy had stayed quietly in the back row for several weeks working on fractions, but now she sat with the group, a robust, eager forty-two students that had dwindled down to the small, chummy arc seated here to do the English lesson.

It's 1978 at Chicago Urban Skills Institute (CUSI), which prides itself on providing a free eight-week module in preparation for the exam in high school equivalency. Students with a 36% average will receive a brown, leather-bound certificate. We meet four nights a week for four hours a night, 5:30 to 9:30, the time of night when I would otherwise feel widowed and bereft.

At the right moment, I step into the scene. "You have fifteen minutes to write using this vocabulary word, and then it's a five minute break," I announce. "Leave your written work on your chair, and move it back into the proper row." This last direction is in case the student decides not to return after break. I do not want to move furniture. I write the word "clinic" on the dusty chalkboard with chalk from my deep pocket.

The class bends to the task. Some use dual language dictionaries. Others strike out boldly on the paper, which I provide from one of my two army surplus metal trunks. CUSI's motto is, "'Round the clock and 'round the year." Mine is, "Anything that makes my evening easier is money well spent."

I glance at the class. Sloe-eyed Josè has stopped writing. "What are you going to do with the last ten minutes?" I ask him. He bows his head, seemingly in heavy thought, but there are no accompanying hand movements.

I place a workbook on each desk and pick up the written assignments.

"Call me kenneth" is in bold block letters at the top of punk rocker Hwader Chang's paper, and I make a note in my attendance book.

Noel (real name Nawah Abdullah) is the epitome of an English gentleman in brown tweed coat with a capelet over the shoulders and beautifully cut slacks. He has written about his two-year stay in London until his accountant brother could bring him here. He's had a bit of a hard time with me, a woman teacher. I can see in his mournful eyes that it's a hard situation for him to endure.

Marvin Stewart, uptown short-order cook, father of several, ex-hillbilly, has written coherently about the clinic where he takes the children. He comes faithfully all four nights a week, stays through reading and language, and leaves about eight o'clock, saying he had better get home, calling a cheery blessing and profuse thanks. He absolutely cannot do simple arithmetic. We don't even talk about it any more.

I have learned never to let a student take a book or workbook home. I would never see the book or the student again. CUSI issues GED workbooks in math, social studies, language and citizenship, which I keep locked up along with multiple copies of old *Reader's Digests* scrounged from a suburban school district and Catholic editions of *Open Court Readers* from the custodian of the school across the street from my house, which is twenty blocks and culturally a million miles away.

Beautiful, blonde, blue China-doll-eyed Stephan Bransen has stayed in during recess. He's wearing a maroon velvet jacket with large pearl buttons, and he carries a briefcase to class. He had been rescued from the sludge pots and dives along Wilson Avenue by an older Spanish woman, a hairdresser who sends him to school, and, although he has been in Special Ed, I think he may just make it. He is asking about a math page we did earlier, talking earnestly to Seam Tan Huot. Seam is my math reference, too. He and his mother and brothers walked across Cambodia to a refugee camp, and he has stayed in my class for two years learning the never-ending mysteries of English syntax and idiom. In his pink and gray argyles, loafers, and corduroys, he looks like the runner in the Grain Pit that he is by day.

Our classrooms are on the third floor in Truman College. At

recess most of the students press LL on the elevator panel, a confusing idiom. At the far end of a subterranean passage is the CUSI office, where attendance has always been, as far as I can tell, all that matters. Federal money is run through the state, to a local bureaucracy for each attendance hour. With little more than the services of Oxana Ferris and her secretary, a Jamaican woman who toted up the attendance records by hand, CUSI underwrote the expenses of building Truman College in the heart of uptown. Now there is a rabbit warren of pale gray cardboard offices and computer terminals for a staff of several dozen. It's far less efficient than it was.

The teacher mailboxes (another euphemism) are manila envelopes in a file cabinet with directives of ingenious grammatical construction. I have endured six directors, as the Spanish lobby protested and received their directorships, followed by a feminine Polish troika, Azia, Bazia, and Sophia, who rolled up their sleeves and turned the place inside out, knocked a little sense into it, and were transferred out for so doing. Who needs accountability?

Most of my small class is returning from recess. Mario has brought me a hot chocolate. He comes very faithfully except for Thursday when he watches a sitcom at home.

Renee Bitwell, a popeyed, mousy woman in a loose coat which she never removes, who speaks so softly that I can only imagine what the syllables might mean, comes in and sits down to look at the comments I've made on her writing. She is very bright, and I have told her so. She rises in her chair, her coat flies apart, her arm extends excitedly as she points and cries, "I agree with you. It is an adjective." Success is sweet.

I used to laugh that I had three Mohammeds and a Ben Hur. But Mohammed Shahish has left. He was muscled into class by a heavy, cigar-chomping uncle who stayed long enough to assure himself that I was a match for his thickset, argumentative nephew. When I called on him to read, he laughed loudly and asked if I thought he couldn't read. I was glad when he never returned.

I seldom feel that way, although I was also glad to see the last of Albert, a retired railroad man. He was a trashcan of odors. I had to tell him that if he didn't wash he could not come in the room. He replied that he only had a birdbath sink in his room and couldn't do better. Svetlana Lemlinsky left because of the odor, and I was sorry to lose her. She was a treasure who worked in the large law firm of Frothy and Glock and had access to their copying machine. She used to copy news stories for us to read. She brought boxes of yellow #2 Dixon pencils and was the light of our lives for a while. Like Alexander, the small Slavic man in the mink hat, Svetlana seriously questioned the American education system.

I question it too. But I know to hang on when Josè says admiringly, "You know a lot, Teacher," when Mumtazl Yasin says, "I want one of them big red words on my paper," when I receive a printed message from "Truly yourly, WLDorel Bates," or when Carlos Pappa, one of eleven siblings back in Guatemala, tells me laughingly that he laughs all the time here in America. He thinks it's such a funny country. He was never allowed to wear blue jeans or patches in his country. In the words of Huel Muni, "I must attempt education step by step until the end of my life."

MARK VINZ

The Former Student

I suppose I should have learned by now. If I stay in my office at
the university in the summer, former students are bound to stop
by – often the ones I don't particularly want to see again, the ones
who start by saying, "Are you still here?"

"Remember me?" The voice comes from the hallway, but even
when it attaches itself to the moon-shaped face in front of my
desk, I can muster only the vaguest recognition. How many years
ago? What course? Back row, dozing – that part's easy. Begins
with an L.

"Darryl," he says, looking a bit disappointed at my blank face.

"Linderman?"

I'm not even close.

"Modern American Novel three or four years ago?"

"Ten years this past spring," he says, eyeing my bookshelves. "I
remember you had a lot to read."

"Well, I've added a few books, though I still keep most of the
good ones at home." Darryl doesn't crack a smile. He's a lawyer
now, back on campus for a conference and taking a walk to check
the old place out. Why else would he be wearing a coat and tie in

this heat?

"You'll be glad to know I've started reading again," Darryl breaks the silence. "What's his name, the guy who wrote *Hawaii*. Kinda reminds me of that book we read in your class. Something with an animal in the title."

We go though the list, from *One Flew over the Cuckoo's Nest* to *The Sirens of Titan* (Darryl thinks a siren is some kind of animal), settling finally on *Rabbit Run*.

"I never read the whole thing," he announces. "Just enough for the quizzes. I bluffed the question on the final. You still give comparison and contrast?"

Darryl grins shyly front of me as if this is something he's been waiting years to tell me – until I tell him I always keep a few extra copies of certain books, especially novels, and I probably can find an old *Rabbit* if he'd like to get around to finishing it. But when I poke through the books on that particular shelf, it's not there and, fidgeting toward the door, Darryl looks relieved. He has to get back to his conference but not before he's shown me a photo of three nondescript blond children on a backyard swing set.

"It might have been a better picture if you had more of the kids and less of the swimming pool," I tell him, already feeling disgusted at my own pettiness.

After Darryl has gone, I stare at my bookshelf's books awhile, especially at a few of the most familiar volumes – which came from another former student a long time ago.

🍎

His name was John. He came to my office one summer simply to say hello, and before he left we'd talked about half a dozen books and made plans for a tennis match. John had been in a couple of my literature classes a few years before, and I still remember the first words he ever said to me: "I don't look much like an English major, do I?"

He didn't, I had to agree – the heavily muscled of a body-builder, the close-cropped hair of an ex-Marine, both of which he was. But that's where the stereotype stopped, for John was one of those students it's a pleasure to remember. He acted the way I've always supposed an English major *should* act. Not only did he always have something intelligent to say in class, he actually read some of the books from the "suggested reading" list.

The summer John walked into my office was after he'd been teaching high school English and coaching football for a couple of years in a town somewhere in the far reaches of the state. He had decided to come back to pick up certification for teaching driver's education. "Even in Podunk you've got to diversify if you want to keep your job," he said. "Besides, we were 3-7 in football last year."

That summer and the next one, when John returned for more classes, I got to know him as well as I've known any of my former students. We continued to talk about books and teaching, and he even showed me a couple poems. "I know I'll never really be a writer," he said, "but it can't hurt to try. At least it gives me a sense of what happens on the other side of the page."

After those summers we'd exchange letters once in awhile. John had found a teaching job at a bigger school; he'd also gone through a very painful divorce. And then, probably two years later, not long after his school district laid him off in a round of budget cuts, he stopped by my house in command of a large U-

Haul truck containing everything he'd managed to salvage from his former life. Quite simply, there didn't seem to be anywhere else for him to go now. He'd decided to move back to a place where he'd been happy and look for a new job – one outside of teaching.

For a while at least, our acquaintance seemed to resume as though he'd never been gone. But it wasn't long before John's life was changing so much that I didn't see him very often. He found a job selling insurance; he found a woman to get serious about, too – a widow with small children – in a local parents-without-partners group. Soon enough, John and the widow were married, and then I hardly saw him at all. "You know how it goes," he would say whenever I bumped into him. He was always cheerful, full of news about his job and family, but there was something else, too, something that made me sadder each time I saw him.

It was on another summer afternoon a couple of years after John moved back to town that he showed up at my office door again, lugging an enormous box of books. "My wife's tired of moving these around," he said. "No place for them in the new house, so I thought I'd just give them to you – for your students. Maybe you'll even find one or two you want to read yourself."

I tried to talk him out of it, of course, but his new life made arguing impossible. "Not even room in the basement?" I remember saying. "Couldn't you put up some shelves in the basement?"

I read in the local paper some time later that John had taken a job in another state. I clipped the notice but then managed to lose it. And now, as I look again at my bookshelves, I can't help wondering about the students who got John's books. I did try keeping a list for a while, but it eventually got lost somewhere too.

As I look out the window, shadows are stretching toward late afternoon. I should probably get to work on a course syllabus.

🍎

"Are you still here?" was what Darryl said.

Better yet, maybe I should look for something to read. How long has it been since I've read something I wasn't teaching, anyway? Maybe I should check those shelves again – before it's time to go.

SHELLEY KITTREDGE FROST

Charming the Bridge Over the River

I was trying to think of new experiential activities for my students beginning English as a Second Language, most of whom were from Mexico and Central and South America. My students weren't quite ready to visit the local retirement home to play vocabulary games. With its added cross-generational dimension, that activity had worked great for my advanced class. But they needed more than the usual dinnertime visit to a fast-food chain to practice ordering burgers and fries.

I knew that the best way to learn a language is to practice it with native speakers. I pondered where I could get a roomful of willing Americans. A church? A theater? A city council meeting?

Then it hit me. At the same time every evening, while my class of native Spanish-speakers was meeting to learn English, a class of Americans was meeting just across the hall to learn Spanish. It was more than a river that divided these two groups of people. Language, culture, preconceived notions – all represented potentially daunting borders.

I cornered the Spanish class teacher, Tracy, during break. He was intrigued by my idea and decided to help me pull it together.

The next night, I stood in front of my twenty-five students with a hammish grin. "Tonight we're going to practice our English someplace new," I said. "Follow me if you want to have some fun." With arms waving, I started out the door, my class behind me, whispering and laughing.

Across the hall, Spanish Conversation 1 held a roomful of curious American eyes and smiles. My group sat down to the side as I joined Tracy at the front of the room.

"Good evening, everyone!" I said. "We have something special in store for you tonight." I gestured toward my class, "We have a whole group of people here who want to learn English. And a whole group of people here," waving to Tracy's students, "who want to learn Spanish. Would you agree that the best way to learn any language is to practice speaking it?"

Nods, smiles, yeses.

"Here's what we'll do. I'd like everyone to pair up with a partner from the opposite class: one of my students with one of Tracy's students. After we're all paired up, we'll start some conversations and get to know each other. But here's the catch. For the first ten minutes, you can speak only Spanish." I paused for effect. "That's everyone – speaking only Spanish, no English. After that, we will spend ten minutes speaking only English – no Spanish, just English. The ten minutes after that, you can speak whatever you like – English, Spanish, whatever."

The two different worlds slowly got up and merged, stepping over aisles, jostling bags and jackets, until everyone had a partner. A few hellos and handshakes, a smattering of chuckles.

I had picked Spanish to be spoken first because my class represented the visiting culture, on several levels, and I wanted them to be able to be themselves. And to hold the first position of power, as it were.

There was Luis, a meteorologist from Uruguay who in America had to work at both a local drugstore and fast-food restaurant to make the money that he sent home to his wife in South America. There was Ana from El Salvador who hadn't finished the sixth grade; she was now a housekeeper in a nearby home. There was shy, middle-aged Josè from Mexico who worked in a restaurant and liked to play soccer. All of them were challenged here in this country, frequently and worst of all by a prejudicial undercurrent that assumed most immigrant Hispanics were second-class citizens who had come here to leech our social, health, and welfare programs dry.

Faced with this, along with other political and familial pressures that had followed them from their homeland, my students were trying to make the most of their situations. Most were striving to become productive residents of their communities, coming to class four nights a week after long workdays to learn one of the most difficult and erratic languages on the planet – English. I knew nearly every one had an admirable work ethic, warmth, and humor, not to mention the homemade tamales and cookies they'd give to me at Christmas.

Tonight they had come as visitors to this classroom of mostly white, wealthy, well-educated Americans. These native English speakers seemed friendly and open. But they were inarguably an integral part of the host culture, with all of its condescending misconceptions.

The first ten minutes, then, the room started filling with Spanish words, some broken, some lyrically fluent.

"Como se llama Usted?" faltered Nancy, dressed in a business suit and holding her textbook closed on her lap.

"Me llamo Josè," smiled Josè. "Como se llama Usted?"

"Me llama Nancy," she said.

"Me llamo," suggested Josè, holding out his hand. "Mucho gusto."

"Me llamo Nancy. Mucho gusto!" They shook hands and laughed. This part was universal.

But the powerful thing was this: Josè was Nancy's teacher this evening. He was in the position of educational and interactive superiority as he nodded encouragement and occasional corrections. The same was true for all my students here. Certainly I'd never seen them this confident or relaxed. They were in their linguistic element, and they nobly rose to the task.

The Manhattan Beach locals had their turn next. Everyone spoke only English for ten minutes in similar, friendly exchange.

"All right, Josè," smiled Nancy. "How many brothers and sisters do you have?"

"I have two brothers," said Josè, holding up two fingers.

"No sisters?"

"No sisters. Zero. And you?"

During the last ten minutes, everyone continued their small talk in whichever language they wanted to practice. Some were engaged in more animated conversations than others, but everyone was talking.

We all left with gifts that night. My students had been given the opportunity to coach their American hosts while speaking their native tongue and demonstrating generosity and kindness. The native-English speakers had gotten the chance to interact with a group of unknown immigrants – about whom they may or may not have had negative preconceived ideas – in a uniquely simple and positive context. What I received – and it has stayed with me through the years – was the joy in thinking that the next time a student of either group walked down the street and encountered someone of the opposite culture, they would remember the experience of this night.

Thomas C. Popp

A Hasty Conclusion

I was lecturing on fallacies to my Critical Thinking class, telling them of the red herring fallacy. "Criminals – usually escaped prisoners – would drag a piece of smoked fish across their trail to divert the searching bloodhounds. That is where the name 'red herring' is derived from..."

Ironically, our topic was diverted by a plump, little work-aid barging into my classroom. With a smile she handed me a stack of purple-sheeted memos. Her interruption came at one of those brief moments that I had at least half of the class's attention. I felt a bit guilty for harrumphing at the purple stack in my hand; I had obviously insulted the young work-aid.

It wasn't her interruption that annoyed me as much as it was the topic of the memo that was assumed to be important enough to interrupt my lecture. I shook my head as I read the memo to myself and handed it out to my students. It read:

Continue the Academy's tradition of
a healthy winter with your fellow students.
Be able to relax this cold, dark season knowing that you

won't get the flu! Flu Shots are only five dollars for
Academy students. You should stop by the Learning Center as soon as
possible to make your appointment for a shot.

My agitation got their attention, for my students assumed I would support any document from "the-higher-ups." Several students went as far as removing their personal stereo headphones. One girl who usually spendt the class with her entire body curled into her sketchpad, drawing futuristic love scenes (humanoids embracing each other) sat up and put her drawing pencil behind her ear.

"Well – what?" she asked.

"What? Well, I do not believe in flu shots."

A young man in the far back corner of the classroom with his shoulder rested on the wall wanted me to expand: "Wadya mean, ya don't believe in 'em?"

At this point, all thirty students were holding the purple sheets with both hands and looking down at the memo, then up at me.

"I don't believe in the reasoning behind infecting myself with something that I'm trying to avoid," I told them. "The flu shot is the flu. For several days after you've been given the shot, you will experience flu symptoms. But the idea is that you will become immune to the virus that they have pumped into your blood system. God knows what this developed version of the virus will do to us twenty or thirty years from now."

One of them mumbled, "You ever gotten one?"

"No, though I have had friends and associates who have and told me some horror stories."

Around the room, young heads were nodding in amazement. Being a teacher who thinks on the fly, I took advantage of this moment of attention.

"Does anyone see any fallacies being used in this memo?"

"Appeal to Tradition!"

"Yes, Sara. Explain."

"'Continue the Academy's tradition of having a healthy winter.' They're trying to persuade us to get these shots by telling us that it's a *'tradition.'* The idea that it's always been done this way, so we should continue to do it this way."

Heads throughout the room nodded as if to say 'tsk-tsk' at the administration. They couldn't believe the propaganda in their hands. A lot of them slammed the purple paper down on their desk in disgust.

"Anyone else?"

Javier spoke for the first time in the semester without being coerced.

"*'Only five dollars.'* Isn't *'only'* a 'Weasel Word'?"

"Good, Javier! Yes, I would say in this case, 'only' is being used as a 'Weasel Word.'"

"Anyone else?"

"'You should stop by the Learning Center as soon as possible.' Isn't that...? Uh...? Exaggerating the situation?"

"Yes, Arelis! It sure is. Is there a specific name for a fallacy where one exaggerates the situation?"

James, who had never volunteered a smidgen of class participation, spoke up from the back row. The entire class turned to watch him.

"Well, it ain't really any pecific fallacy," he said as he lifted the brim of his baseball cap out of his face. "Maybe the False Dilemma fallacy cuz they be imply'n that if ya don't get the flu shot 'as soon as possible' then you're gonna experience 'a cold dark season' sted-a-hav'n 'a healthy winter.'

"Excellent, James, and –"

The class looked back at me, but James continued.

"They be use'n that Ad Populum fallacy in da first line. Imply'n dat everyone is doin' it, with 'Continue...with your fellow students.' Da whole damn thang sounds like a bunk sales pitch, dunn'it? I mean, 'You should stop by the learning center.' Yeah! 'Should' is bein' used as one of dem weasel words too! Hell if dey know what I 'should' do."

My students broke their trance from James' rant, unbent their bodies and looked back up at me to continue the rally. Then someone's wristwatch beeped the hour, and they started shuffling their books and bags in order to go.

"Okay everyone. That was a good discussion. We need to keep this type of group learning up, every week. (Several smirked as if to say, 'Yeah, right.') I've said before that we need to take everything we read with a grain of salt. You people were acting as critical thinkers today; just keep it up."

Those who didn't show their disregard for the purple memo by leaving it lying on their desks crumpled it and slammed it into the garbage can as they left. I was happy to see them putting the lessons into action.

The following week, I was at the blackboard preparing for my lecture on Doublespeak: ambiguous words, jargon, and gobbledygook. I finished writing definitions on the board seconds before the class was to begin and went to the door to close it. A few students were missing, so I looked down the hallway for stragglers. There was Sidney, my best student, trudging down the hallway. His usually pinkish face was the color of vanilla cookie dough.

"Sidney? Are you ill?" I asked.

"Oh man, Mr. Clemens. Yeah."

I stepped back, holding the door open for Sidney as he lumbered his way into the classroom.

I admit that I held my breath as the boy passed. He had a frightening presence of disease about him. The whole class watched him with apprehension. He stood for a moment at the head of the class, silent, teetering back and forth a bit.

"Mr. Clemens was right."

Sidney explained how he "was forced" to take the flu shot by his employers. It was Wednesday, and he had been given the shot on Sunday. One student inquired, "Four days later and you still be ill'n?!"

I gave Sidney a caring pat and asked him to take his seat; then I went on with the day's lecture. Every time I looked back from writing on the board, at least one student would be staring at Sidney, slouched in his chair, struggling to push his pen. When the class was writing, I quietly asked Sidney if he wanted to go home. As I expected, he chose to stay, saying he didn't want to get behind.

The following week's class fell on a day of whipping cold winds and falling snow, so I wasn't surprised that nearly half my class didn't show up. Sydney was back with color in his face and his usual attentiveness. I let my students use the day as a catch-up session.

A week later, class met during one of those winter thaws typical in Chicago. Almost all the snow had melted, and it was a balmy sixty-one degrees. But this time more than half my class was gone! Of course, a sunny day is often considered sufficient condition to skip; I credited that to ruining the day's class. What really got my goat were the students who were in class the week before when I gave them time to catch up. They, I assumed, had concluded that they could afford to miss class.

Then I recalled that when I had walked into school, the building had a ghost-town feeling. I had seen only a handful of students sharing cigarettes on the steps outside and just a few couples groping each other by the vending machines.

Poor attendance burns me up and always throws off my excitement for the lesson at hand. I had a twist in my stomach and a stripe of heat down my back that I attributed to that day's low attendance. I even felt a chill running over the surface of my skin. But I pushed through my lecture as well as I could.

I was truly sickened by the lack of student presence. It exhausted me. To top it of, my lecture was rudely interrupted. That same little, round work-aid came crashing into my classroom. A little pink sheet instructed me to visit the head of the department, Mr. Harbuckle, immediately after class. Good, I thought; Harbuckle and I need to discuss the cause of this institution's poor attendance and determine what action should be taken. For the first time in seven years of teaching, I ended class early.

As I entered the office, the administrative assistants and secretaries looked at me as though I was crashing a party. "What have I ever done to them?" I wondered.

I knocked on Harbuckle's big, oak door.

"Clemens? That you? Come in here."

He was perched behind his desk in a red leather chair. The sun shone through the window behind him, catching him on the side of his face, exaggerating his sturdy jaw and glowing cheekbones. He looked downright strong and healthy. Which is why, I assumed, he was quick to notice my lack of spirits.

"Jesus, Clemens. You look horrible. Sit down. Clemens, how was the attendance in your class today?"

"Well, sir, it was upsettingly poor. I don't know what can be done. But it is imperative that we get to the source of the problem and rectify it."

"Ah yes. *The source of the problem.* Clemens, have you noticed how the students here at the Academy seem to be very close with each other. What I mean is that one often sees them sharing the same cigarette or bottle of soda pop."

"Yes, sir."

"Clemens, did you notice the obvious good health of my assistants in the other room, not to mention my own?"

"Well, sir, now that you mention it, yes."

That's when my deductive reasoning began, and I started to see what Harbuckle was getting at. It seems I was the reason for the poor attendance. A flu epidemic had practically leveled the Academy that winter, and it was all blamed on my deconstruction of that damn purple memo.

As I walked back through the administrative offices, past those who had had their flu shots, I recognized the angry glares that would accompany me for the rest of the school year. Then I sprinted to the men's restroom, where I began the first stages of the virus that punished me for the following two weeks: the flu.

CHAPTER SEVEN

Dancing Through Life

A teacher affects eternity: he can never tell
where his influence stops.

—HENRY ADAMS

Beth Walker

Tales from the Tanning Bed

A very pretty cheerleader approached me after class, smiled, and said, "I didn't write my paper for today because I had to go to the tanning bed."

She scanned my skin for sympathy. I was lily-white from a summer basking in the tinted-twilight of my computer. Obviously, I had none to give her.

Though I had only been teaching college freshman composition for two years, I thought I had heard it all. But not this – and coming from this student, of all people. She was the type who was more interested in hair spray than hyperbole, iron men than irony. My only thought at that moment: "Wow. I pride myself on my vivid imagination, but not if I had written all the books in Alexandria could I have come up with the line you have just fed me."

But instead of giving her extra credit for her creativity, I said, "We all have our priorities, now don't we?" and turned to the next student in line. Here I was, twenty-six and already tired of listening to excuses. Was a simple essay too much to ask?

In addition to preparing that day's class activities, I had written a response to my own assignment. I always did.

"Yes, but," my students remind me, "you like to write." For some, I imagine, this is a creepy thought, as if I might as well enjoy cleaning stopped-up toilets at the Louisiana Red Light Truck Stop.

Me? Like to write? I don't know how this myth got started – the one about writing being fun. It's up there with "trying hard should get you an A" and "you can leave after fifteen minutes and not be counted absent." My students think that writing is not fun, yet they still hold fast to the myth that professional writers possess some secret they are not privy to.

Well, here it is: even though I love to write, I don't love to write. It's insane, spending hours pushing a pen across a perfectly good blank piece of paper. I could be throwing the Frisbee around or lying in a tanning bed instead. In fact, every student who announced loudly and proudly at the beginning of the semester that he or she just loved to write (gush, gush) has failed my class.

"Show me. Don't tell me. It's not that I don't believe you, but you haven't turned in anything," I said, wagging my finger at one student who liked my class so much that she failed twice.

I know what she was thinking: "What if it's not any good? What if I've been lying to myself all this time? What if I'm a horrible writer, and everybody knows it but me?" That's what the tanning bed and all those other excuses are for – they cover up fear, resistance.

I remind my students that my writing also gets rejected, sometimes returned with comments so peculiar that the editor must have been not only unsympathetic, but also drunk, asleep and stupid. But that's no reason to stop writing.

So why do I write? Beats grading papers. The very thought of having to write yet again, "Please use paragraphs. Please title your work. Please use a dictionary or spell checker," makes me want to clean toilets for a living. I'm sure the pay would be better. One day I caught myself saying, "Please, God, don't let me finish out my life circling commas." Even though I love to teach, I don't love to teach. That's insane. I could be writing instead.

There is some reward, though. Most of the poems and stories I've published over the last eight years have come from assignments I've given my students. So much for those editors who write in their submission guidelines: "No workshop material, please." What difference does it make where the material comes from, as long as it comes, as long as it's good? Not only does writing with my students give me an excuse to write – when I could be braving the three-day-old brown dishwater instead – it forces me to meet deadlines. Writers everywhere have this problem – starting, then finishing.

"If it's late, it had better be great," I said to one student last semester who said she might have a problem getting her story turned in. "Is it gonna be great?"

She nodded her head, mute as a lone leaf in the wind, then gathered her books. She never turned it in.

"See, I must be psychic," I hear myself saying over tacos to my husband. "I could have bet you five dollars that would happen."

He points out that I always make bets on my students. Too bad writing is not such a sure thing.

Don't get me wrong. I'm often asked if I get bored teaching freshman composition, working with beginners. Of course not. Everyone can stand a lesson in the basics. In fact, I consider myself a beginning writer every time I face the blank page. Like my students, I wonder what I'll write about, how much I can write, whether I'll have to read it aloud in class.

But I get tired of listening to my own excuses. I believe in the process. In the end I have to practice what I preach: "Shut up and write," I say affectionately to my students, not so affectionately to myself. Some days I'm fast and write well. "You wrote that before you got to class, didn't you, Ms. Walker," someone will say after asking me to read mine. "No. Ten minutes. You saw my pen moving." Some days I'm slow and write with great shame. But I have no excuse: no dog ate my paper, then got run over, and the only time I could take it to the vet was during writing time. I write because I must do what I ask my students to do. No excuses. I teach what I do. It's another secret I'm privy to and a sure bet: I've learned more about writing by teaching beginners than I have any other way I know.

After all, it's better to write in the classroom than in a tanning bed.

SARAH A. POWLEY

Pencilhead

Some years ago, the guidance counselor appeared at my classroom door with a senior boy in tow. We were already three weeks into the first quarter, and my basic English class of eighteen kids was a cohesive and productive unit. I would have preferred it to remain that way.

She pulled me to the side. "There is no place for him," she said. "His schedule's been changed, and he needs English. Will you take him?"

Everything I had heard about him was true. He wouldn't do his homework. He tried to sidetrack discussions with impertinent remarks. His body language said, "You can't make me!" and on Friday afternoons he jingled the coins in his pockets and spread the money he had collected for 'partying' out on his desk for the class – and me – to see.

I started with the money.

"Put that away," I said. To his own surprise, I think, he cleared his desk.

Slowly – it took all semester – he began to settle down, to speak pleasantly, to read his assignments. He started to take tests seriously, too, although he would protest the unfairness of each one, just in case he failed.

His contribution to discussion was less and less often an outburst, but even in December, he still didn't raise his hand.

At the semester's end, he needed a new class. The one I would teach next was a step up in difficulty, and there would be thirty students. He asked what it would be like.

"There will be more reading," I said, "and you'll have to raise your hand. You won't be the center of attention."

He considered this. "Okay," he said, "but you'll never make me a 'pencilhead.'"

"Pencilhead," of course, was a derogatory term for a smart kid.

"Pencilhead" didn't become a scholar overnight, but he did earn a B in the class. His mother said in June that he'd read more books that year than in all of his years of school combined. I will never forget the day he pulled his chair into another group's reading circle so he could hear a second discussion of the book his group had just talked about.

After he graduated, he joined the military. He served overseas, and once he wrote me that he was taking an English course – "Introduction to Writing."

Eventually, he returned to the community, gained employment, and went on for post-secondary training. For a few years, he occasionally came to school to see me. He always gave me a hug. He had become a success, and he told me I'd taught him that he could accomplish anything he set his mind to.

In truth, his success had more to do with him than me. He had decided to grow up that year in my classroom.

But we teachers remember students like "Pencilhead" long after they have left school, and their stories become our personal folklore. We recall such stories to nourish and reward ourselves for the work we have done.

Most of us go into education hoping to make a difference in someone's life.

"Pencilhead" stories tell us we have.

BRAD HAKES

One Lone Teacher and
His Trusty Red Pen

If there's any truth to the horrors and controversy of school life as portrayed by Hollywood and a pessimistic media, I can be thankful for my first year of teaching. No deaths, no shootings, no suicides, no blackmail, no threats, no student-teacher affairs, no teacher-teacher affairs, no fights and no asbestos. Of course, maybe none of this happened because I was teaching college English instead of high school in the inner city. I escaped my first year with nothing more than a handful of nervousness, a depressed student, one young mother, a thief and 320 comma splices.

I was 22 when I first stepped to the other side of the teacher's desk. Almost all of my students were straight out of high school. It was like being an older student in the class but pretending to have vastly greater authority and knowledge. The only problem was that I had to prove this by lecturing intelligently and coherently for seventy minutes at a stretch. In the first couple of weeks I discovered I could accomplish only one of these goals at a time. I would have something good to say, but my advice failed as it became vocal. For example: "Start with your idea in mind, but also start while thinking about the structure of the whole. So the first thing you want to do is think about both of these, but don't do one before the other. Er, does that make sense?" Or, going for clarity, I would share advice that they learned in grade school and say something like, "An important tool to creating a strong structure in your essay is to indent each paragraph." Wow. They really got their tuition's worth on that one. And yet, some still forgot to indent.

Most of this bad lecturing ended when I learned I should prepare for each class. But that didn't end another of my bad habits, which was the attempt to make jokes, especially at the start of class. As one of my fellow first-year teachers said, "I feel like a stand-up comedian who is bombing."

I had the idea that I should teach the way late-night television hosts open their shows. I pictured myself bounding into the classroom like Conan O'Brien and then shaking students' hands like Jay Leno, as if students would be crowded around my desk to shake my hand. Then (and this is the only part I actually did) I tried to open the discussion with some witty comment about the president or a joke about some famous person.

I am happy to say that these opening comments sometimes did get some laughs, but when they didn't, there was no sidekick to fill the silence. (Note to other young teachers: never make jokes about boy bands in front of college freshman girls – they still take it seriously.)

Eventually I learned to do what I was paid to do: teach. All was good between the troops and their leader.

Then the real world hit one of my students particularly hard. A relative of this student had been in a serious accident. Between visits to the hospital and bouts of depression, my student missed the next week of class.

The week after, she entered my office as though she had just come from the morgue and was crying by the time she sat down. Hmm, where to start – your writing is good but grammar needs some work, you could participate more in class, or try not to miss any more days of class?

The discussion sounded more like, "...yes, you can still pass the course. Your writing's fine – just make sure you turn in the rest of the assigned papers, and don't fall too far behind. I know you can do it. Hang in there." Despite missing more classes during the last third of the semester because of her own health troubles, she did pass.

🍎

One of my students the next semester was a single mother, as I found out when she turned in the first writing assignment. If she was older than me, it wasn't by much. In the first couple days of class, I noticed her because she often voiced her opinions, and the other students listened. I think we all recognized her common sense intelligence.

We didn't see her again until the eleventh week. Except for the first essay, she hadn't turned in any other assignments, and she never made the effort to tell me why she wasn't at class. When she returned in the eleventh week, I was ready to tell her to withdraw from the course or fail it.

After class I asked her to follow me to my office, where I gave her the options. She returned with, "I was going to withdraw, but if I do, I lose my scholarship for next semester. And if I don't pass the class, I will have to stay for an extra two years because I have to take certain classes in order. Plus I've had so many other things to do this semester. First I had to move to another apartment. Then my daughter was sick for a while. I've already written most of the papers and just haven't turned them in – is there any way I can still pass this class?"

A two-year delay because of English 101, which is offered twenty times each semester? It didn't seem likely, but I would rather believe a lie than fail a student who has stumbled through some bad luck. I told her to hand in the rest of her assignments before the end of the semester and attend every class from now until the end for a chance to pass.

During the twelfth and thirteenth week she was at every class and, as before, was creating good discussions. After that she disappeared again, never to return or turn in any more papers.

🍎

That same semester I had a handful of foreign students in my class. Some were good at writing papers in English, and others were not. I told them that our English department had a section of beginning English for ESL students, but they all wanted to be enrolled as "normal" students competing with everyone else. For some of them this meant half a semester of essays written with the clarity and grammatical correctness of middle school kids and written about subjects like "The Process of How Much I Love My Family." Then, when their papers were returned with poor grades, they asked me how they could be doing so poorly when they were getting As in computer science.

In the last few weeks of the semester one of these students handed in a paper about "dogma and axioms as they pertain to

America today." Yeah, right. This six-page paper was two and a half pages longer than the required length and was grammatically perfect. It was the type of paper that a college freshman might think is exactly what the teacher is looking for. It sounds academic, it uses big words, it has abstract concepts and, besides, anything with "axioms" in it must be good.

If this were the first paper the student had handed me, I might have believed that he was a perfectionist trying to impress me with encyclopedic knowledge. Knowing that this student could barely patch together a well-written paragraph, I guessed he had either stolen this piece or had someone write it for him (I imagined him saying, "...and make it sound smart, too!").

To make sure I didn't accuse anyone wrongly, I showed the piece to a few other English teachers. They laughed at the hoax and the fact that a student had claimed to write it.

I asked the student to meet with me after class. I didn't know if he was aware of the consequences of plagiarism, but I had learned I could recommend that he be expelled from school. Since he was a foreign student, expulsion meant deportation.

"Did you write this paper?" I asked him once we were in my office.

"Yeah," he said.

"Really?"

"Yeah."

"Then what do you mean by the axioms of America? What are the axioms of America?"

"It says there in paper. You don't understand what I mean?"

"No, I don't think you understand what you mean. I don't believe you wrote it. Can you even tell me what this paper is about?" I asked this question partly because I didn't know.

"There. You have to read paper. Then you understand."

"Can you show me a draft or something that proves you wrote this?"

"I typed it into computer first time. And then I'm finished."

"At the beginning of the semester I asked you to show drafts for every paper..."

"Wait. I want to ask question."

"Go ahead."

"All my other classes I get straight As. Then I get low Cs in this class. Why is I'm not getting As too? Maybe you need to talk to the other teachers, and they tell you I get As."

For the next hour he changed the subject and denied any possibility that he took the paper from somewhere else. I couldn't call him a cheater unless I could prove it, and that was nearly impossible.

At the end of our session, I told him I wouldn't grade his paper until he showed me a rough draft or research on the topic. By then he remembered making a rough draft but thought he threw it out already. He was going to go through his garbage to see if he could find it.

The next week he came to class with the assignment's "real" essay in hand. The one he turned in before was an accident; it was for another class, he said.

🍎

As for the comma splices, a lot of red marks went into correcting those mashed sentences, by the end of the semester I think the students had learned from their mistakes.

RICHARD HAGUE

Trouble, Mess, Disaster

I know that all of matter is in conspiracy against me and will try to trip me up whenever it can: the sweeper cord, despite my pains, tangles on the only piece of furniture in the entire room, the garbage can lid sticks so that I drop the whole load of chicken bones and dog poop I'm trying to toss, my shoelace breaks when I'm late for a meeting. Nevertheless, I cherish trouble, messes, and disasters because I know the unexpected opportunities they present, the utterly surprising obstacles that make me dance my way through life rather than bulldozing a heedless path.

When I was a kid sometimes I would do something that perturbed my dad so much that he would send me to my room for half the day. I would mope around for a while, feeling sorry for myself, but then I would figure out some project to work on – organize my insect collection, read a book about beetles, daydream about the Amazon. What would have started out as the punishment for some trouble I'd brewed often turned into a pleasant afternoon of solitary busyness. Trouble transformed, became a fresh opportunity.

🍎

Messes – those piles and avalanches and dumps of stuff that life accumulates – also offer rich opportunities, not just frustrating obstacles. For example, there was a dump near the pond we boys often visited. During most of our adventures nearby, we steered clear of that fouled hillside of trash rolling down from where trucks could back up and disgorge their clots and slides of trash. The stuff glinted with dangerous shards of glass, ragged sheet metal, and exhaled the fumes of old paint cans, turpentine, creosote, the ashes of a burnt outhouse. But one afternoon, I surveyed the smoking spill of debris and eyeballed the skeleton of an old Whizzer motorbike, its back wheel still intact. That back wheel with its welded flange became the central component of a bike I built with a friend, and which afforded us several rich lessons about, among some other serious things, tools, work, freedom, power, and perseverance.

🍎

Similarly, nearly forty years later, rummaging around in the basement, I came across a single Victorian porch post, the bottom foot of which was riddled with termite damage, but the upper six or seven feet of which was perfectly solid, if in need of some major painting and scraping.

The moment I saw it, I knew we could tear off the rotting makeshift deck on the back of our recently acquired house and rebuild a grand Victorian veranda around this beautiful architectural relic. My wife and I have since spent most of our free time in warm weather on that porch, its posts newly painted, the salvaged one solid at the center of the roof beam.

Even disaster may yield goodness if the gods that day are favorable, or if the sun-spot cycle is right, or if we are in a state of grace, or just lucky. When my first marriage collapsed, I began a series of summer hermitages in the country, living alone and getting to know ticks, raccoons, puff adders, tulip poplars, blackberry hillsides and four generations of my neighbors. The travails, despondencies and enlightenments of those difficult days gave me, over years of recollection and recovery, most of two books of poems, half a book of essays and a dozen short stories. Not a bad haul from what looked more like a tragedy than treasure.

And now I see that I've tried to make my teaching more like some of that, too – messier, less linear, not always predictable, and so apt, at least sometimes, to surprise and wonder. I want my students to dance, too, not plow their way with cold logic and steely intellect alone through literature and life, building high walls against confusion and doubts and sudden turns of luck. I want them – and me – to be a little lost now and then, so that when we do at last find our ways, they will be our ways, not someone else's. We will have knowledge and lives we have constructed ourselves, not hand-me-downs already worn out by others.

This is not to say that there is no place for tradition in learning, but rather to point up that there is no place for thoughtless conformity to convention in the discovering and shaping of an original life.

Those who never get into trouble, who do not have the gifts of messes and disasters now and then in their lives, live poorly and meanly despite their extravagantly safe existences. They starve on the empty abundance of success while us lucky ones, bloodied, black-eyed, limping a little, emerge from the burning barns of our lives with wild grins on our faces.

"Damn, " we say, standing up straight once again, knocking the ashes from our jeans, and positive that we're the better for having survived. "Damn," we say, "a little more of that just might of kilt me entirely."

About the Authors

"My Students and Their Essays" 3
John Guzlowski, a 2001 recipient of the Illinois Arts Council Poetry Award, teaches Poetry Writing and Contemporary American Literature at Eastern Illinois University. His poems have appeared in such journals as *Atlanta Review, Negative Capability* and *Madison Review.* He has also self-published *Language of Mules,* a book of poems about his parents' experiences as slave laborers and displaced persons in Nazi Germany during and after the Second World War.

"Let's Fight" 5
Barbara Somers taught eighth and ninth graders for years, then got a graduate degree in social work and worked in a private office for mental health. Combining her twin interests in social work and education, she worked in a ghetto middle school for three years. She is the co-author of *Talking to Your Children About Love and Sex.* She also wrote a column for a local newspaper on parenting after divorce.

"No Wonder Your Paper's so Short!" 9
Juliana Gray Vice is a recent Ph.D. graduate of the University of Cincinnati, where she has taught English composition and poetry writing. She has also taught composition at the University of Tennessee. Her poems have appeared in such journals as *Sewanee Theological Review, Yemassee* and *Alabama Literary Review,* and she has a nonfiction essay forthcoming in *The Oxford American.* She currently lives in Russellville, Arkansas, where she teaches English composition at Arkansas Tech University.

"Human Race" and "Callers" 11, 81

Barbara A. Rouillard is a teacher and writer from Springfield, Massachusetts, whose poetry and short stories have appeared in over eighty-five publications, including *Yankee, Amelia, Midwest Poetry Review, Happy, Writer's Journal, ByLine* and *Verve.* A special education teacher at West Springfield Senior High School since 1983, Barbara has also recently completed a creative non-fiction manuscript entitled *Whosoever Brings Them Up* – a book about the lives of her students.

"Chips off the Block" and "Filed but not Forgotten" 21, 95

Melinda Stiles taught high school English in Wisconsin and Michigan for twenty-one years. She retired before she burned out and moved to Idaho to write. Her work has been published in *The Kalamazoo Gazette, Sun Magazine* and *Woven on the Wind,* an anthology by and about western women.

"Some Things You Can Teach" 25

Jessica Gates Fredricks is the music teacher at Bethune Academy, a K-5 science and technology magnet school in Haines City, Florida. Earlier, she was director of bands at Santa Fe High School in Santa Fe, New Mexico. She has received numerous grants and awards for her music-based movement programs, including the AT&T TeachNet grant, the Florida Elementary Music Educators Association Creativity Grant and two grants from the Teacher to Teacher Connection for innovative classroom programs. Her cross-disciplinary program, *Composers in the Classroom,* took a Top Program Award at the 2000 Disney Teacheriffic Awards. She is her school's Teacher of the Year for 2000-2001 and the Polk County East Area Educator of the Year. Her articles have appeared in *Education Digest, School Band* and *Orchestra and Teaching Music,* the magazine of the Music Educators National Conference. She served as editor for the book *Letters from the Front.*

"The Magician" 29

Franz Weinschenk started teaching in 1948 at Edison High School, a school in Fresno, California, where many minority children attended. After a stint in the U.S. Army during the Korean War, he moved over to Fresno City College where he has been an instructor and a dean and still teaches a couple of classes. Besides having been published numerous times, he is the originator and host of a popular, award-winning radio program over public radio in the San Joaquin Valley called "Valley Writers Read."

"Unspoken Gratitude" 31

Lisa Johnson's nine-year career has included a year overseas teaching English to Hungarian high schoolers, four more teaching English and Creative Writing to tenth and eleventh grade Connecticut students, and a brief stint as a tour guide/teacher to Japanese people visiting the Big Apple. She has also published pieces in *Natural Health, Big Apple Parent,* and *Small Town Life* magazines, and won Breastfeeding.com's 2000 Fall Story contest.

"The Greatest Gift" 35

Bruce Birkemeyer taught high school social studies and speech communications for thirty-six years in Iowa and Wisconsin. During that time he coached debate and speech students through many forensics contests. He now is a judge at the Iowa High School Speech Association State Speech Contest and at the Future Farmers of America State Speech Contest. He has written a humorous choral reading about school kids having the flu called, "Influenza," and a satire on the human condition in response to the recent school shootings in the form of a reader's theatre titled, "The Garden Club." He is currently working on a philosophical duet acting piece questioning the origins of man and religion, which will be called, "Homework."

"I Hate Schools" 41

Carolyn S. Kremers writes literary nonfiction and poetry, and lives in Fairbanks, Alaska. She has served on the faculties of the MFA/ Creative Writing Program at Eastern Washington

University in Spokane, the English Department at the University of Alaska Fairbanks, and the College of Rural Alaska in Bethel. Before that, she taught music and English language arts, grades 1-12, in public schools in Chicago, Colorado and Alaska. Her book *Place of the Pretend People: Gifts from a Yup'ik Eskimo Village* (from which "I Hate Schools" is taken) was published by Alaska Northwest Books in 1996. Essays and poems have appeared in numerous publications, including *American Nature Writing 1999*, *Brevity, Creative Nonfiction, Manoa, Newsday, North American Review*, and *Runner's World*. Currently Kremers is completing a second nonfiction book, *Then Came the Mustang*, and seeking a publisher for her book of poems, *A Thin Birch*.

"A Teachable Moment" 63

Beverly A. Buncher is the middle school principal of the Samuel Scheck Hillel Community Day School in North Miami Beach, Florida. She has taught all ages from newborns through adults. Her specialties in secondary school were middle school English and journalism. After a few years of elementary school teaching, she ran a home-based Head Start Parent-Child Center for moms and their children aged birth through five years. She has written articles published in parenting and educational magazines and journals. She also co-edited a *Multicultural Guide to Parenting Practices with Dr. Stephen Bavolek* for Family Development Resources, Inc., Park City, Utah. Mrs. Buncher has been writing for publication since her teen years, when she was editor-in-chief of the *Taylor Allderdice Foreword* and a weekly columnist for the *Pittsburgh Jewish Chronicle*.

"A Brightly-Lit Room" (excerpted from "Teachers") and "High Plains Drifter" 67, 147

Michael O'Rourke is an assistant professor of English at Tennessee Tech University. His narrative essays, on a wide variety of subjects, have appeared in *North American Review, Gettysburg Review, Michigan Quarterly Review, Cream City Review, Cimarron Review, Isle* and other journals.

"Too Late for Miss Roselli" 71

Priscilla Long teaches writing at the University of Washington Extension and elsewhere. She is author of *Where the Sun Never Shines: a History of America's Bloody Coal Industry* (Paragon House, 1989). Her work appears in *The Journal, Passages North, The Southern Review, North Dakota Quarterly, The Seattle Review, Passages North, Southern Humanities Review* and elsewhere. She has an M.F.A. from the University of Washington and serves as senior editor of (www.historylink.org).

"For Beth" 77

Benjamin Scott Grossberg is Assistant Professor of Creative Writing and Literature at Antioch College in Ohio. He recently completed his Ph.D. at the University of Houston. His poems have appeared in journals such as *Paris Review, Malahat Review* and *Nimrod,* as well as a number of anthologies. He is currently finishing his first book of poems.

"Breakable Ashley" 85

Rebecca Kaiser began teaching when she was thirty-eight. Her first job was at Lansingburgh High School in Troy, New York, where she taught General Science classes. She quit that job to work in an alternative middle school with at-risk youth. When that program was cancelled, she moved to Troy High School, where she now teaches Regents Biology.

"A Little Hopeful" 87

Jeffrey Lee has published a poetry chapbook with Ashland Poetry Press, *Strangers in a Homeland* (at www.ashlandbookstore.com), and his works have appeared in *CrossConnect, Crab Orchard Review, Many Mountains Moving,* etc. A poetry CD of his is forthcoming from Drimala.com. He has taught at Community College of Philadelphia, Franklin & Marshall College, Camden County College, Rutgers University, etc.

"Tutoring with Richard"   101
James Hein is a tutor for the Fiction Writing Department at Columbia College in Chicago. His fiction and poetry have been published in *Spire Magazine, Poetry Motel, Xpressions Journal, Hare Trigger, Bowwow* and others. He is currently working on a novel entitled, *For the Love of the Dead.* James lives in Lake in the Hills, Illinois.

"Empty Gesture"   107
Marilyn Bates is a consultant at the University of Pittsburgh and a retired teacher from Mt. Lebanon High School where she taught Creative Writing. She is also a "Poet in Person" in the Pittsburgh schools for the International Poetry Forum. Her works have been published in *The MacGuffin, Pembroke Magazine, Carnegie Mellon Magazine, The Paterson Literary Review, Santa Clara Review* and *Voices in Italian America.*

"Miss Hotchkin, Racist"   117
Vicki Salloum earned an M.F.A. in Creative Writing from Louisiana State University in Baton Rouge. One of her stories has appeared in an anthology on women and aging, *When I Am An Old Woman I Shall Wear Purple.* She resides in New Orleans, where she has taught as an adjunct professor at four colleges and universities. She now works as a business manager for a legal publication.

"Remembering Winter"   135
Carolyn Howard-Johnson is the author of *This Is The Place,* a novel about love, prejudice and redemption set in Utah. It was released in 2001 by America House, Baltimore. "Remembering Winter" is creative nonfiction from her new collection of short titles called *Harkening.* More information is available at www.tlt.com/authors/carolynhowardjohnson.htm

**"A Curmudgeon's Book of Lists: Take Two" and
"Trouble, Mess, Disaster"**   143, 195

Richard Hague has taught writing, literature and interdisciplinary studies at Purcell Marian High School in Cincinnati since
1969; the writing program he designed and administers won the
National First Place Award for "Excellence in English" from the
English-Speaking Union in 1994. He has published seven collections of poetry including *Possible Debris,* (Cleveland State
University Poetry Center, 1988), *Ripening* (The Ohio State
University Press, 1984), and *Greatest Hits: 1968-2000* (Pudding
House Publications, 2001). His *Milltown Natural: Essays And Stories
From A Life* (Bottom Dog Press, 1997) was nominated for a
National Book Award in nonfiction. He has been a Scholar in
Nonfiction at Bread Loaf, an NEH seminarian at Oxford
University and has twice been awarded the Master Teacher Award
from the faculty of Purcell Marian.

"Chicago Urban Skills Institute, a Valiant Effort, 1978"   153

Marion Stern began a long and varied career in teaching in 1937
in the Winnetka Public Schools, when things were simple and
direct – truly, the olden days. Her most recent publication was a
memoir about her family's summer compound in Highland Park
in *Northshore Magazine.* She has been happily engaged in drawing,
writing and gardening since she turned seventy and would caution any young readers: plan well for your retirement – it may be
longer than you think.

"The Former Student"   159

Mark Vinz is Professor of English and co-director of the Tom
McGrath Visiting Writers Series at Minnesota State University
Moorhead, as well as the first (1995-98) coordinator of MSUM's
Master of Fine Arts in Creative Writing program. He has taught
at the university since 1968. His poems, stories, and essays have
appeared in numerous magazines and anthologies; his most
recent books include *Late Night Calls: Prose Poems and Short Fiction.*
He is also the co-editor of two anthologies of Midwestern litera-

ture published by the University of Minnesota Press (*Inheriting the Land* and *Imagining Home*), both of which won Minnesota Book Awards, and three anthologies published by New Rivers Press: *Beyond Borders: New Writing from Manitoba, Minnesota, Saskatchewan, and the Dakotas; The Party Train: An Anthology of North American Prose Poems;* and *The Talking of Hands: Unpublished Writing by New Rivers Press Authors* (also winner of a Minnesota Book Award).

"Charming the Bridge Over the River"   165
Shelley Kittredge Frost is a professional writer, editor, and web site developer who enjoys serving a diverse group of clients through her communications business, ReVampEditing.com, and publishing articles in various magazines, including *Self* and *The Aesthetic*. Continuing to value the powerful dynamic of cultural exchange, she considers her years teaching ESL at the South Bay Adult School in Redondo Beach, California, some of the most fascinating and rewarding of her life.

"Hasty Conclusion"   171
Tom Popp received an M.F.A. in Creative Writing from Columbia College in Chicago and is certified in the Story Workshop® method of teaching creative writing. He is a workshop director and a teacher of specialty writing courses in the Fiction Writing Department at Columbia College and also teaches English composition, critical thinking, and creative writing at The International Academy of Design and Technology in Chicago. He is a columnist and the fiction editor for *Velocity* magazine.

"Tales from the Tanning Bed"   181
Beth Walker is an adjunct instructor of English at The University of Tennessee at Martin and at Dyersburg State Community College. For the past eight years she has taught freshman composition, developmental writing, and writing to students enrolled in intensive English programs. She holds the M.A. in Creative Writing from The University of Tennessee, Knoxville and is certi-

fied by the National Writing Project. Author of two plays, a collection of short stories and a novel, all unpublished and unloved, she has published more than forty poems in journals such as *New Millennium Writings, Alaska Quarterly Review,* and *Cream City Review.* Her work also appears in the 1996 anthology of Tennessee writers, *Homeworks.*

"Pencilhead" 185
Sarah Powley teaches English at McCutcheon High School in Lafayette, Indiana. Her essays have been published in regional magazines and professional journals. She is a 1993 recipient of the Milken National Educator Award.

"One Lone Teacher and His Trusty Red Pen" 189
Brad Hakes is a Teaching Assistant at Minnesota State University Moorhead, where he is working toward his M.F.A. in Creative Writing. His creative efforts are mainly invested in poetry, short fiction and photography. Several of his poems have appeared in *Red Weather.*